GEOLOGISTS' ASSOCIA

THE LAKE DISTRICT

by F. MOSELEY

With contributions by—

M. J. Branney,
N. Bowden,
A. H. Cooper,
N. Davies,
P. D. Guion,
R. H. Hunter,
E. W. Johnson,
N. S. Jones,
D. J. D. Lawrence,
D. Millward,
M. G. Petterson,
D. E. Roberts,
R. J. Suthren,
B. C. Webb,
B. Young.

Edited by C. J. Lister and J. T. Greensmith

© **THE GEOLOGISTS' ASSOCIATION**
1990

Notes. *The details of routes given in these guides do not imply a right of way. The onus of obtaining permission to use footpaths and to examine exposures rests with the user of the Guide who should carefully observe the Code for Geological Field Work, issued from the Librarian, The Geologists' Association, c/o Department of Geological Sciences, University College, Gower Street, London WC1E 6BT.*

In particular, those in charge of parties should ensure that there is no indiscriminate hammering of, or collecting from, exposures and that no damage is caused to property.

Any information (e.g. change in footpaths, filling in of quarries, threat to SSI's, new exposures) that would update and improve a revised edition of this Guide would be welcomed by the Association.

CONTENTS

ITINERARIES

INTRODUCTION

F. Moseley, Birmingham University

Since Mitchell's (1970) G.A. guide to the Lake District there has been a great deal of new work which has resulted in fundamental new interpretations of much of the geology. During this time the ideas of plate tectonics have been developed and the place of the Lake District in the evolution of the ancient Iapetus Ocean discussed. Many of the enigmatic structures of the Skiddaw Slates are now seen in a new light and the nature of the Borrowdale "volcano" is much better understood, as are the sequences and events of the upper Ordovician and Silurian sediments (Windermere Group). It has therefore been necessary to produce a new guide, and to expand it to incorporate the new work. It is now virtually impossible for one person to cover to any reliable depth every part of Lake District geology, even though the whole region is no more than 50 km in diameter, especially so when one considers the wide variety of the geology involved. This includes the stratigraphy, palaeontology, palaeoecology and sedimentology of rocks from Cambro-Ordovician to Carboniferous age, the petrology and geochemistry of volcanic and intrusive rocks, and complex structures such as those of the Skiddaw Slates. This guide is therefore multi-author with each itinerary produced by an expert on the ground. The object was certainly to cover equally all the main divisions of Lake District geology, but inevitably there are omissions, partly where land ownership problems have proved difficult, and partly because authors were not available for some areas. It will also be noticed that there is a concentration of excursions west of Ambleside. This is because much of the new work by the Geological Survey and university research workers has been in this region. The guide is designed to be used in conjunction with suitable topographic maps. The best are the 1:25,000 Ordnance Survey Outdoor Leisure maps, and failing this the 1:50,000 Landranger Series. I must also thank Carl Burness and Jackie Stokes who prepared most of the text figures in the drawing office at Birmingham University. Some other diagrams were prepared by those responsible for itineraries.

The Lake District is an extremely popular tourist area, with its beautiful scenery of lake and mountain, but it is an environment that can easily be damaged by those who fail to apply "the country code". It is therefore important to stress at the outset that observance of the code for geological fieldwork issued by the Geologists' Association, is of supreme importance. Indiscriminate hammering must be avoided, specimens should be taken only if they are required for further study, litter should be taken away, gates closed, walls should not be climbed, permission should be sought when visiting private land, and great care must be taken on the mountains. Mountain rescue teams turn out many times each year to save those who have been foolish and perhaps misjudged the "gentle British hills". The weather can indeed change in less than an hour from warm and sunny to cold and wet with thick cloud. Good maps, a compass, adequate waterproof clothing, spare food and a first aid kit are all essential for walking across the fells, and a hard hat will be necessary for quarry visits.

THE GEOLOGY OF THE LAKE DISTRICT

F. Moseley, Birmingham University

The overall geology of the Lake District is illustrated by figures 1 and 2. The literature describing this geology is voluminous and I do not intend to survey it at this stage, but references will be found in the itineraries, in the bibliography at the end of the book, and for all the earlier work, in Smith's bibliography (1974).

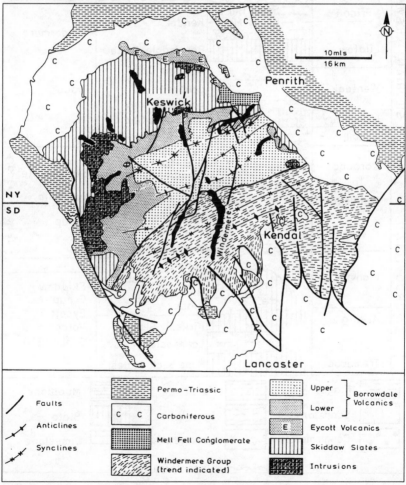

Figure 1. A generalised geological map of the Lake District.

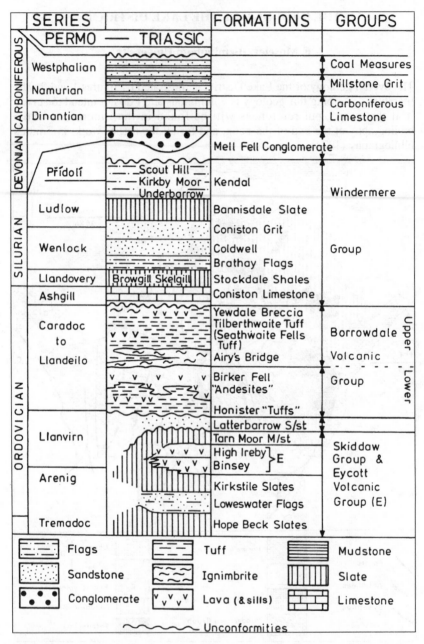

Figure 2. A generalised geological succession for the rocks of the Lake District.

It is now necessary to set the geological scene, with an outline of the geological history, followed by a more detailed account of the main rock groups. The Lake District is dominated by rocks of Lower Palaeozoic age, and to understand their origins we have to visualise a perspective of world geography half a billion years ago, first during Ordovician and later during Silurian times.

It was a world with no land vegetation, and a geography very different from that of today. Most reconstructions indicate an ancient ocean (Iapetus) at about 20° south, with England, Wales and Southern Ireland on the south-eastern margin, and Scotland and Northern Ireland many kilometres away to the north-west. Since the hypothesis was first advanced by Wilson (1966) there have been many different models (see Figure 3), including a suggestion that the ocean may not have existed (Mason, 1988). The Lake District formed part of the active margin of the south-eastern continent and the main stratigraphic divisions reflect this. The oldest rocks, the Skiddaw Slates, were formed as turbidites on submarine slopes with extensive slumping and all the other sedimentary structures associated with this environment. The Eycott and Borrowdale volcanoes were both essentially of calc-alkaline composition, and typical of volcanics associated with subduction at active margins, much as the Andes and Japan are today. Towards the end of the Ordovician palaeontological evidence, particularly, reveals that the great ocean had virtually closed so that Scotland and England were irretrievably joined, as were Northern and Southern Ireland. There were large batholithic intrusions about this time, and a widespread unconformity as the shelf seas of the Coniston Limestone spread across the eroded remnants of the old volcanoes. It will be understood that these generalisations are still under discussion and new hypotheses appear every year. The Silurian was a period of almost continuous subsidence, and thick turbidite sequences were laid down in elongate "geosynclinal" basins. The main continental collision phase of the Caledonian Orogeny occurred during the early Devonian when the Lower Palaeozoic rocks were subjected to severe folding, cleavage and faulting, and the second stage of the Lake District granitic batholith was emplaced (Bott, 1978). The well known Shap Granite is one surface expression of this intrusion. Details of the general palaeogeographies of those times, including ocean closure and continental collision, have been much discussed (Figure 3; Anderton, 1982; Cocks and Fortey, 1982; Dewey, 1982; Faller and Briden, 1978; House, 1968; Mason, 1988; McKerrow, 1982; Soper and Hutton, 1984; Soper et al., 1987; Stillman, 1984). However, such details, although of considerable interest, are not essential to this excursion guide. There followed a transformation in the ancient geographies with the formation of the Old Red Sandstone or Eur-American desert continent, crossed along its southern and eastern margins by the Caledonian mountains. The intermontane basins of the Lake District area, in an environment not

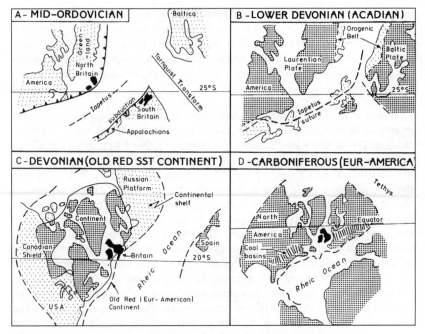

Figure 3. Outline palaeogeographies from the Ordovician to the Carboniferous.
The maps are modified and simplified from various sources, including
Anderton, 1982; Cocks and Fortey, 1982; Dewey, 1982; Faller and Briden, 1978;
House, 1968; Mason, 1988; McKerrow, 1982; Soper and Hutton, 1984;
Soper *et al.*, 1987; and Stillman, 1984.

unlike that of present day Iran or south Arabia, received the thick deposits of
the Mell Fell Conglomerate (Capewell, 1955; Wadge, 1978). The next
important event was the deposition of the Carboniferous Limestone in
shallow tropical seas, which gradually encroached onto the older rocks of the
continent (Mitchell, 1978). It was followed by the deltaic and estuarine
Millstone Grit and Coal Measures formed on a continent which now
straddled the equator, and then as the British area moved steadily north, by
the arid northern hemisphere deserts of the Permo-Trias. During Mesozoic
and Tertiary times the modern Atlantic Ocean was opening and a tensional
regime developed resulting in a complex of normal faults, but also in the
gentle warping which formed the Lake District dome. After a long time gap
(there are no Jurassic, Cretaceous or Tertiary rocks in the Lake District) the
Lake District mountains were carved into their present form by the glaciers
of the Quaternary ice ages. The details indeed are much more complex than I
have indicated, but I will attempt to fill in some of them by commenting on
each major rock group.

LOWER PALAEOZOIC

Skiddaw Group

The Skiddaw Group is composed almost entirely of turbidity current derived siltstone and mudstone (slate) with subsidiary greywacke sandstone. The Group is mainly of Arenig age, with some Llanvirn and is now known to extend down into the Tremadoc (Molyneux and Rushton, 1984; 1988). These rocks have always been difficult to interpret for several reasons. Where details can be determined the structures are complex but there are also considerable areas of uniform mudstone in which bedding is not easily seen, and the structure and sequence problematical. Fossils are also scarce which makes determination of the detailed stratigraphy even more difficult, although incredible perseverence by a few collectors in the field over many years has made it possible to erect a meaningful zonal sequence (Jackson, 1961, and Molyneux and Rushton, 1984, 1988 and in press). This is based mostly on graptolites, but acritarchs and other fossils have also been extremely useful. As an example it is worth noting that less than 10% of several hundred localities sampled for microfossils have actually yielded specimens. It is mostly where there are interbeds of sandstone that some order can be seen in the sequence and structure. It is mainly where sandstones are present that new ideas have been developed about the origins of many of the structures (Webb and Cooper, 1988 and in this volume itineraries 4-6). Although the general stratigraphical sequence has been disputed (Simpson, 1967) I believe that most would now accept that shown in outline on Figure 2, based on Jackson (1978), Wadge (1978) and earlier workers, but like most other facets of the Skiddaw Group, work now in progress will probably involve modifications. It has been accepted for more than 20 years that the Skiddaw Group has been subjected to polyphase deformation. The consensus was that moderate folding preceded the deposition of the Borrowdale volcanics (F_1), followed by several phases of deformation related to the main early Devonian Caledonian orogeny. The alternative view was also expressed that the real orogenic deformation of the Skiddaw Group was pre-Borrowdale volcanics (Simpson, 1967; Helm, 1970). The interpretation of the structure has now changed. It has long been known that the Skiddaw Group is of turbidity current origin with all the sedimentary structures associated with that type of environment, including a great deal of slumping. Webb and Cooper (1988) have now extended this concept and regard the majority of the early small scale folds, previously regarded as tectonic (F_1), as slumps (but not soft sediment). They have also been able to map out olistostrome rafts which occur particularly within the Buttermere Formation (itinerary 5 and Webb and Cooper, 1988). These are large blocks hundreds of metres in diameter which slid downslope prior to the deposition of the Borrowdale volcanic rocks. This new work immediately explains several of the problems which have bedevilled understanding of Skiddaw Group structures.

Interpretation of the early (F_1) folds as slumps, with which Roberts (itinerary 2) has expressed agreement, invalidates the requirement for a pre-volcanic tectonic event, although Webb et al. (1987) prefer to see the main Lake District anticline as at least initiated at this time (their F_2 in part). The variable orientation of these folds has always been difficult to understand in tectonic terms, but slumps are less likely to have constant orientations, and where their trends are north-easterly they would be tightened and develop an axial plane cleavage during the main Caledonian orogeny (now F_3, Webb and Cooper, 1988). The folds are also smaller in scale and more complex than tectonic folds in similar Silurian lithologies (the Bannisdale Slates), and this fits a slump hypothesis better. Even so, it is difficult, when examining outcrops in the field, to point to undoubted features which distinguish between slump and tectonic folds. The current British Geological Survey mapping project has also given rise to the suggestion that there are three sedimentary environments within the Skiddaw Group which are separated by major E.N.E. shears (Cooper, in press). The central environment contains the slumped olistostromes around Buttermere, and is separated from the northern zone (slumps only) by the Causey Pike Fault. However, as yet I see little evidence for the southern zone.

Although it now seems likely that no severe tectonics preceded the formation of the Borrowdale Volcanic Group, it is nevertheless separated from the Skiddaw Group by an unconformity representing the F_2 deformation in part (see page 22). This junction has been discussed many times by different authors (see page 22), and described as conformable, disconformable, and strongly unconformable with a major orogenic episode separating the two groups. I do not intend to occupy space by giving details of these discussions except to say that recently Branney and Soper (1988) suggest that the unconformity may reflect regional uplift connected with the generation of andesite melt during Iapetus subduction, whereas Webb et. al., 1988, believe that it represents, in part at least, the initiation of the Lake District Anticline.

Summarising, it would seem likely that the Skiddaw Group, several thousand metres of turbidites, was deposited on the continental slopes of the Iapetus Ocean and developed, in particular, small-scale slump structures and large olistostrome rafts, which became detached from time to time, resulting in juxtaposition of materials of quite different ages in a chaotic manner. No wonder there have been so many paradoxes in stratigraphical and structural interpretation of the Skiddaw Group.

Eycott Volcanic Group
In former years the Eycott volcanics were thought to be part of the Borrowdale volcanics. However, Downie and Soper (1972) showed that they were distinctly older when they recorded fossiliferous siltstone and mudstone interbeds of upper Arenig and Llanvirn age in the lower part of the volcanics,

indicating a conformable relationship. However, Cooper (in press) has described a cross-cutting unconformity between Skiddaw Slates and Eycott Volcanics, but this may be no more than local instability common in volcanic terrains. It does not alter the fact that the Eycott Volcanic Group is older than the Borrowdale Volcanic Group and almost certainly of equivalent age to part of the Skiddaw Group sequence farther to the south (Figure 2). The Eycott Volcanic Group is transitional between calc-alkaline and tholeiite in composition (Fitton and Hughes, 1970). Elsewhere the Borrowdale Volcanic Group is underlain by Llanvirn siltstones, mudstones and tuffs of the *Didymograptus murchisoni* zone (Wadge, 1972).

Borrowdale Volcanic Group

There is no doubt that the Lake District is dominated by the Borrowdale volcanics. They form all the spectacular mountains and the glaciated valleys of the most popular tourist areas. Of course the present day topography in no way resembles that of the Ordovician "volcano", and the question arises as to whether its original shape can be reconstructed. It was certainly a subaerial structure (Branney, 1988), and until recently no marine fossils had been observed. Molyneux (1988) has now recorded acritarchs of possible Caradoc age from Holehouse Gill (itinerary 13). Since estimates of the total thickness of the volcanic rocks have generally been in excess of 5000m is tempting to think of it as an upstanding cone rather like many of the present day calc-alkaline volcanoes. However, this is unlikely to have been the case, certainly for much of the period of the eruption (itinerary 19), when a large part of the 600 square kilometre area seems to have been dominated by fluviatile and lacustrine environments, with isolated volcanic centres. There is also new evidence that substantial parts of the volcano were subjected to caldera collapse, which induced volcano-tectonic faulting, block tilting and the foundering of the volcanic pile (itinerary 17, Branney, 1988a; and Branney and Soper, 1988). Such areas are of great complexity and can only be unravelled by extremely detailed mapping. They do, however, contrast with other areas which were mantled by uniform spreads of volcaniclastic sediment (mostly "bedded tuff") with little structural complication.

Other recent and continuing work has been by E. W. Johnson, D. Millward, M. G. Petterson and B. Young (British Geological Survey) and by M. J. Branney, N. Davies and N. Mathieson (Sheffield University). In the south-west the British Geological Survey team in particular have been able to divide the sequence of this large area into three phases of activity, which are as follows:

1.   Early volcanism dominated by effusion of basalt to andesite flows and sills with interbedded primary and reworked pyroclastic deposits. The lenticular form of many of the units has made it very difficult in the past to establish a unified stratigraphy. However, the resurvey has identified several

important and distinctive marker horizons that permit the establishment of a coherent stratigraphy. The entire lava pile is assigned formally to the Birker Fell Formation. The structures within the clastic deposits, the distribution of the flows and presence of several palaeovalleys indicate the construction of a broad shield-like volcanic field. Important features of the formation are illustrated by itineraries 7 to 12.

2.   Eruption of widespread and voluminous acid and, commonly strongly-welded, pyroclastic deposits associated with volcano-tectonic faulting. The steep unconformities are described in itineraries 10 and 12, and part of the sequence is examined in itinerary 15.

3.   Deposition along a possible piedmont belt of thick epiclastic volcanic rocks interbedded with widespread intermediate to acid ignimbrites. Early Caradocian marine sedimentary rocks occur in the lower part of this sequence (itinerary 13). The higher part is visited during itineraries 14 and 15.

The age of the Borrowdale Volcanic Group as a whole has always been difficult to determine and being underlain by Skiddaw Slates of *murchisoni* age (Llanvirn) and overlain by the Coniston Limestone Formation of Ashgill age in the Lake District, but upper Caradoc in the Cautley and Cross Fell areas, has generally been regarded as Llandeilo. However, micro-palaeontological work by Molyneux (1988), suggests that the whole of the volcanics could have been erupted during the Caradoc, although the evidence is not conclusive.

The range of rocks includes all those to be seen in modern calc-alkaline volcanoes, including basalt and basaltic andesite, normal andesite, dacite and rhyolite. Lavas and pyroclastic rocks are almost equally represented, although some of the former are now interpreted as sills, and much of the latter is volcaniclastic sediment rather than true tuff. The lavas and sills are generally massive and form crags, whereas the more easily eroded "tuffs" form the intervening benches. Evidence for sills is normally found at their top contacts since in most cases they were intruded at shallow depth into unconsolidated water-laden ashes, and display structures (peperite etc., Branney and Suthern, 1988) difficult to account for with a lava interpretation. Most of these structures can only be seen to advantage in working quarries where really fresh surfaces are exposed, and I would warn against a sudden rush to re-interpret most of the lavas as sills. Other determinations of sills come from detailed mapping where a cross cutting structural relationship can be demonstrated (itinerary 15). The lavas show most of those structures to be seen in modern lava flows. They may be flow-jointed (basalts and basaltic andesites mostly), frequently they are flow brecciated where the front and top of the lava cooled before the interior became solid and was then disrupted into blocks by pressure from the still flowing interior. Such flows can easily be mistaken for a coarse pyroclastic deposit. The tops and bottoms of flows are often amygdaloidal with vesicles generally filled with calcite and chlorite. Recently Allen *et. al.*,(1987) showed that there is still much more to know about the "lavas" by their descriptions of composite flows, which require an extremely detailed examination of the sequence, although Branney and Suthren (1988) have now reinterpreted the most prominent of these as a sill.

Pyroclastic rocks include volcanic breccias, airfall and water-lain "tuffs", and ignimbrites. The former often have metre sized fragments, grading down to coarse tuffs (lapilli tuffs) with centimetre-sized fragments, and were laid down moderately close to the eruptive vent. Resembling them are the volcanic mudflows (lahars), distinguished by their polygenetic nature lack of bedding and poor sorting (itinerary 9). Airfall tuffs are often bedded and can on occasions be difficult to distinguish from volcaniclastic sediments formed by fluviatile or lacustrine processes. The latter, however, usually display the distinctive sedimentary structures characteristic of deposition in or by water, such as current ripples, various types of cross-bedding, grading, horizontal and convolute lamination, flutes, load casts, flame structures, and there are slump folds and faults on a variety of scales. Surge deposits are also present (itineraries 11, 18 and 21). They are generally thin, cross-bedded, and commonly resemble other types of bedded tuff. A generalised field term of "bedded tuff' is, however, used for all these bedded deposits since the field relations are often inconclusive, and their interpretation can then be a matter of speculation, whilst there would also be too many categories to show on small scale maps. Ignimbrites are completely different and have received much attention in recent years. Until Oliver's work (1954) they were believed to be rhyolite lava, but are now well established to include a wide variety of pyroclastic flows from lava-like welded tuffs to incoherent non-welded ash. In composition ignimbrites are predominantly acidic, but can vary from rhyolitic to dacitic and andesitic. Most of the Lake District ignimbrites are strongly welded with a flinty appearance, weathering white. They generally exhibit a eutaxitic texture with dark fiamme (flattened devitrified pumice fragments) giving a streaky appearance easily identified in the field. Detailed mapping has made it possible to divide sequences into cooling units (say 50m thick) which in turn can be subdivided into flow units. Columnar cooling joints are seen at a number of localities and there are nodular beds believed to be late-stage vapour phase products.

Windermere Group
All the predominantly sedimentary rocks from the upper Ordovician to the end of the Silurian are included in the Windermere Group (Moseley, 1984). The component formations shown on Figure 4 will be described briefly from oldest to youngest.

16   F. MOSELEY

SERIES			FORMATIONS	MEMBERS
PŘÍDOLÍ			KENDAL FORMATION	SCOUT HILL FLAGS / KIRKBY MOOR FLAGS / UNDERBARROW FLAGS
LUDLOW	SILURIAN	GROUP	BANNISDALE SLATE FORMATION	
LUDLOW			CONISTON GRIT FORMATION	YEWBANK SANDSTONE / SHEERBATE FLAGS / POOLSCAR SANDSTONE
WENLOCK			COLDWELL FORMATION	UPPER COLDWELL FLAGS (= HORTON FLAGS) / MIDDLE COLDWELL MUDSTONE (= STENNERLY MUDSTONE) / GAWTHWAITE SANDSTONE
WENLOCK		WINDERMERE	BRATHAY FLAGS FORMATION	
LLANDOVERY			STOCKDALE SHALES FORMATION	BROWGILL / SKELGILL
ASHGILL	ORDOVICIAN		CONISTON LIMESTONE FORMATION	ASHGILL SHALE / TROUTBECK (Phacops mucronatus Beds) / WHITE LIMESTONE [INCLUDES RHYOLITIC TUFF] / TORVER (Phillipsinella Beds) / HIGH PIKE HAW (WEST) APPLETHWAITE (CENTRE & EAST) / (Calymene Beds) / STILE END [INCLUDES YARLSIDE RHYOLITE] / LONGSLEDDALE

Figure 4. Major stratigraphical subdivisions for the upper Ordovician and Silurian rocks of the Lake District (the Windermere Group). The Coniston Limestone names in upper case are those of McNamara (1979). The names in lower case are those of Marr (1916b) where they differ from McNamara's names. From Moseley 1984. Note that Přídolí is now preferred to Downton.

The Coniston Limestone Formation, which rests unconformably upon the Borrowdale volcanics has been described most recently by McNamara (1979) and Lawrence *et al.* (1986) (itineraries 22, 23 and 24). The early classification of Marr (1916b) is regarded as essentially correct, but some of the terminology has been changed to fit in with present day stratigraphical nomenclature. Figure 4 retains the classification of McNamara (1979), excepting that his "group'" and his "formations" have been downgraded one level to become a formation and members. The sequence is complex with a great deal of lithological and facies variation, and in fact a substantial part of it is not limestone. There are also significant non-sequences within the succession, particularly above the Torver Member and the rhyolite ash, but they cannot be determined without detailed knowledge of the fauna.

The lowest member of the Coniston Limestone Formation (Longsleddale) consists of breccia, conglomerate, sandstone, siltstone and chert, ranges from 1 to 60m in thickness and rests on an irregular surface of Borrowdale volcanics. Occasional brachiopods and trilobites are to be found, but the clasts are almost entirely derived from the volcanics, so that on first acquaintance it is easy to think one is dealing with Borrowdale volcanics.

The overlying Stile End Member, only present in the east, consists of calcareous siltstone and some sandstone, and contains fossils such as *Calymene, Pteria* and *Orthis*. The Yarlside or Stockdale "Rhyolite" overlying the Stile End beds occurs in the east of the Lake District, approaching 200m at its thickest, and is now interpreted as a rheomorphic ignimbrite (Millward and Lawrence, 1985).

The most important member of the Coniston Limestone Formation is undoubtedly the Applethwaite, with its lateral equivalent, High Pike Haw. It consists of about 50m of nodular limestone and calcareous mudstone, with interbeds of laminated volcaniclastic siltstone forming easily identified outcrops, and in places is very fossiliferous with *Calymene, Acidapsis, and Phillipsinella* particularly common. Upwards the beds become less calcareous, whilst the High Pike Haw Member is essentially calcareous siltstone. The Torver Member (Marr's *Phillipsinella* beds), about 6m thick, is gradational from the Applethwaite, and is cleaved mudstone with occasional calcareous nodules and with much fragmentary fossil material. There is a non-sequence between the Torver Member and the overlying White Limestone (McNamara, 1979) with the latter followed by a thin rhyolitic tuff (actually volcaniclastic siltstone). The limestone is white-weathered, about 2m thick, and is only sporadically exposed. Another non-sequence separates these deposits from the Troutbeck and Ashgill Shale Members, with the former very thin and badly exposed (Marr's *Phacops mucronatus* beds) and the latter, up to 20m thick, low in calcium carbonate and poorly fossiliferous.

As far as field mapping is concerned the junction between the Ashgill and Skelgill beds forms a convenient boundary between the Ordovician and the Silurian. In the west of the Lake District, however, the lowest zone of the Skelgill beds is indicated by a *Glyptograptus persculptus* fauna (Hutt, 1974-5; Rickards, 1978), which is now internationally classified within the Orodovician (see Lawrence *et al.*, 1986). The lithological contrast of the Ashgill Shale and the Skelgill beds also suggests there may be a small non-sequence between them, whilst the *persculptus* zone is missing in the east. The overlying parts of the Skelgill and Browgill beds (about 50m) are of Llandovery age and have been divided into 15 graptolite zones by Rickards (1970,1973,1978) and Hutt (1974-5) with the former mostly black mudstones and the latter more massive grey-green mudstones with black graptolitic laminae. The succeeding Brathay Flags, about 300m thick, are uniformly grey with alternating parallel laminae of paler siltstone and darker mudstone, and graptolitic horizons determined to be of Wenlock age. There is an upward passage into the Coldwell Formation (about 500m thick) with the development of greywacke sandstone and siltstone inter-beds up to 1m thick. The lower and upper Coldwell beds are separated by a band of silty calcareous mudstone (middle Coldwell) which can be traced across the entire Lake District, whilst the upper flags are laminated siltstones not unlike the

Brathay Flags, and are generally placed at the base of the Ludlow Series. The succeeding Coniston Grits, about 1700m of turbidites, are gradational both at the bottom and the top. The sandstone beds are generally 1 to 2 metres thick, and are usually separated from each other by thin mudstones, whilst grading is well developed as are bottom structures such as flute and groove casts. The sedimentary structures indicate sediment transport directions, at least in the area of Coniston Water, of NE-SE (along the axis of the "geosynclinal" trough) and NW-SE, at right angles to it (Norman, 1963).

The Coniston Grits are transitional upwards into the Bannisdale Slates, with decrease in the sandstone component. The latter are about 1000m thick, and have a distinctive lithology of dark mudstone with pale siltstone laminae, and being more ductile than most of the underlying formations, are more strongly cleaved, and are deformed into small scale-folds. The sequence is completed by upward passage into the predominantly flaggy lithologies of the Kendal Formation (Moseley, 1984) which, for the most part, yields a Ludlow fauna, with the ostracod *Frostiella groenvalliana* from the Scout Hill ·Flags indicating a Přídolí (Downton) age at the top (Rickards, 1978).

DEVONIAN AND CARBONIFEROUS

Devonian
The Mell Fell Conglomerate (Figure 2) is strongly unconformable upon the Lower Palaeozoic rocks, and is itself overlain unconformably by Carboniferous Limestone, but otherwise there is no precise evidence for age. The most comprehensive account has been by Capewell (1955), but that of Dakyns *et al.* (1897) should not be discounted. Wadge (1978) summarised the information available up to that time and discussed the estimates for the thickness and derivation of the deposits. Suggestions for thicknesses (275 to 1500m) depend on interpretations of the bedding, whether there is cross stratification or not, whilst the derivation depends on the composition of the pebbles. It is probable that the lower estimate of thickness is more likely to be correct (Wadge, 1978), whilst the composition of the pebbles, which are mostly of Silurian greywacke, points to a mainly southern derivation at a time when the Silurian outcrop extended much further north than at present. There are however some Skiddaw type and Borrowdale volcanic pebbles which suggest westerly sources. Wadge (1978) in fact envisages the deposits as produced by coalescing fans from the south and west. Outcrops can be inspected in the Ullswater region (itinerary 1).

Carboniferous
Carboniferous rocks form a rim surrounding the Lower Palaeozoic rocks of the Lake District and are an integral and important part of the geology of the region. Unfortunately they are not fully covered by the excursion guides, partly because there are problems of access to the land and partly because

authors were not available. However, itinerary 1 includes a few Dinantian localities from the east and itinerary 24 covers part of the Cumbrian coast.

A. Dinantian

The early classical work of Garwood (1907, 1913 and 1916) laid the foundations to the study of the Carboniferous Limestone of north-west England, and his detailed stratigraphy is easily applied to the present day stages (George *et al.*, 1976; Mitchell *et al.*, 1978). By early Carboniferous times the Caledonian mountains had been reduced to an area of moderate relief, with the sea encroaching onto the old arid to semi-arid land mass unit; by the end of the Dinantian, the whole of the Lake District was covered. The sequence is predominantly limestone and is interpreted as a series of cyclothems (Ramsbottom, 1977).

Figure 5 is an outline of the sequence. The Courceyan at the base is represented by the Basement Beds; conglomerates and sandstones, with the Cockermouth basaltic lavas in the north (Macdonald and Walker, 1985). The clastic rocks filled irregularities in the old land surface and are therefore extremely variable in thickness, over 200m in the south-west, about 10m at Shap and completely absent in places.

The Chadian stage is essentially limestone (Figure 5), with Garwood's algal band believed to represent the mid-Chadian regression (Ramsbottom, 1977). Various rugose corals, including *Thysanophyllum pseudovermiculare* occur in the late Chadian (itinerary 1).

The succeeding Arundian limestones are considered to be a transgressive phase and formed a continuous shelf across the southern Lake District. They were followed by regression at the end of the Arundian represented by sandstones in the east, and by sandy, partly dolomitic limestones in the south (the Gastropod Beds of Garwood, 1913). There is a rich coral fauna including *Caninia, Lithostrotion and Palaeosmilia.*

The most striking transgression in northern England is that of the Holkerian (Mitchell *et al.*, 1978). Much of the pre-Carboniferous land surface was inundated by the sea and the shoreline was towards the centre of the Lake District. Important fossils are *Lithostrotion minus* and *Davidsonina carbonaria.*

During the Asbian two major cycles have been recognised but macrofossils are scarce. This stage is perhaps most notable for its spectacular limestone scenery with a widespread karst topography of clints and grykes (Waltham, 1974). It is probable that the whole of the Lake District was covered by the sea by the late Asbian.

The Brigantian Stage saw a great change in the sediments deposited and in the fauna. A Yoredale facies developed in a broad shallow sea, with a strong clastic source in the north-east. The typical Yoredale cyclothems of

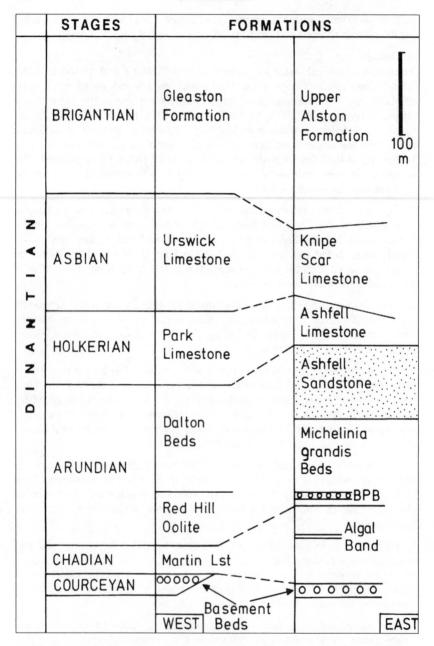

Figure 5. The Dinantian sequence in the Lake District, after Mitchell, 1978

limestones, shales, sandstones and thin coals are best developed in the east with limestone becoming dominant further west. Just above the base there is a distinctive algal horizon, the *Girvanella* bed (Garwood, 1913), whilst the faunas are rich, and include *Lithostrotion, Lonsdaleia, Orionastraea, Palaeosmilia* and *Gigantoproductus*.

B. Namurian and Westphalian
The Upper Carboniferous outcrops mostly in the north and west and is partly covered by itinerary 24.

The Namurian varies in thickness from zero to 300m (Ramsbottom, 1977) and is of Millstone Grit facies in the south, where *Eumorphoceras* and *Cravenoceras* have been recorded, but occurrences are limited, and of Yoredale facies in the north, with *Gastrioceras cumbriense* at the top of the sequence. It is likely that the Lake District massif formed an extension of the Askrigg Block, separating these two facies.

The Westphalian, outcropping only in the north and west, forms part of the Pennine Province of the Coal Measures (Mitchell *et al.*, 1978). At its maximum the sequence consists of rather more than 600m of productive measures followed by several hundred metres of red beds. The productive measures occur as cyclothems of marine shale, non-marine shale, sandstone and coal, each cyclothem representing the building up of a delta (Mitchell *et al.*, 1978). Fresh water bivalves are common fossils and include *Carbonicola, Anthracosia, Naiadites and Anthraconauta*.

The end of the Carboniferous was marked by the Saalian phase of the Hercynian earth movements, which elevated the region and allowed oxidation to take place in a tropical environment.

Permian and Triassic
The Permo-Triassic rocks occur in the Vale of Eden, along the Cumbrian west coast and the shores of Morecambe Bay. They are referred to in itinerary 24 (Cumbrian coast), whilst the general geology has been most recently described by Arthurton *et al.*, (1978). The Hercynian uplift of the Lake District produced a mountainous terrain that included several subsiding basins, resulting in much lateral variation in the sediments. The mountains were progressively buried so that by the end of the Trias the St. Bees Sandstone extended over most of the region (Arthurton *et al.*, 1978).

The lowest (Permian) deposits were breccias (the Brockram) which formed as screes and alluvial fans flanking the mountains of the Lake District and the Pennines. The Penrith Sandstone is thought to have formed as a sand-sea deposit in the intermontane basins, and at its margins interdigitates with the Brockram. Evaporites occur in both the Vale of Eden and along the Cumbrian coast near the base of the St. Bees or Eden Shales. They include gypsum and anhydrite, which formed in sabkha and desert lake environments.

The division between the Permian and the Trias is arbitrarily taken at the base of the St. Bees Sandstone. The sandstone is over 150m thick, dull red, and has been widely used as building stone. It is regarded as an alluvial plain and braided river deposit and was probably continuous with similar deposits south of the Lake District. The highest part of the Trias belongs to the Mercia Mudstone Group and is everywhere badly exposed.

STRUCTURE

The Lake District has been affected by Caledonian, Hercynian and post-Triassic earth movements of which the Caledonian were by far the most important.

It has been established for some time that the Caledonian Orogeny in the Lake District can be roughly divided into the three phases of pre-Borrowdale Volcanic, pre-Coniston Limestone and early Devonian, with much of the tectonic activity related to subduction, the closure of the Iapetus Ocean and the resulting continental collision. In recent years there has been much new work which, whilst not changing the overall pattern has certainly resulted in modifications to previous interpretations.

The earliest "phases" were pre-Borrowdale Volcanic. Points of controversy include structures in the Skiddaw Slates, and the nature of the Skiddaw Slate-volcanic junction, which has always been controversial. There have been strongly contrasting arguments to explain the nature of this junction in particular; (i) that it represents an unconformity of orogenic proportions with intense folding and cleavage before the start of volcanicity (Simpson, 1967; Helm, 1970), (ii) that it is essentially conformable (Soper, 1970), and (iii) that it represents a minor unconformity with a degree of small scale folding prior to the volcanics (Jeans, 1972; Roberts, 1971; Wadge, 1972; Webb, 1972; Moseley, 1972; Soper and Moseley, 1978). Until recently the consensus has favoured the last, with small scale pre-cleavage folds preceding the formation of the volcanics. Now, however, the pre-cleavage folds and other structures are interpreted, by Webb and Cooper (1988) (correctly I believe) as slumps and slides (see above and itineraries 4 to 6) which means that the field evidence for them as tectonic structures has been removed. The unconformity, however, still demonstrably exists, shown by the variable age of the Skiddaw Slate immediately below the volcanics, which ranges from upper Llanvirn in the east to Arenig and Tremadoc in the west. Clearly great thicknesses of Skiddaw Slates were removed before the onset of the Borrowdale Volcanics. Branney and Soper (1988) suggest this may be attributable to uplift resulting from rising subduction-related magma, whereas Webb et al., (1987) believe it may indicate initiation of the main Lake District anticline.

The second "phase" resulted in the well-documented unconformity beneath the Coniston Limestone. It is most easily seen south-west of Coniston where the limestone crosses the axial trace of the prominent Ulpha syncline (Figure 6, SD205905). The syncline must therefore have been formed in pre-Coniston Limestone times (Soper and Numan, 1974). Further south-west the limestone oversteps the volcanics completely to rest on Skiddaw Slates. This can be explained by erosion of the volcanics followed by deposition of the Coniston Limestone Formation on a gently undulating surface. Ingham *et al.*, (1978) indicate that the limestone transgression was from north to south with a possible horst in the south, but this has been challenged by Firman and Lee (1986), who suggest that a large part of the concealed Lake District batholith

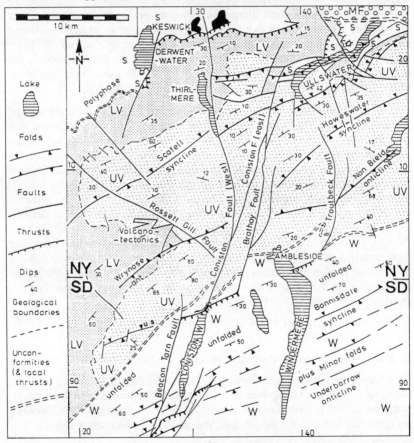

Figure 6. Structural map of the central part of the Lake District. S - Skiddaw Slates, LV - Lower Borrowdale Volcanics, UV - Upper Borrowdale Volcanics, W - Windermere Group, MF - Mell Fell Conglomerate, US - Ulpha Syncline.

could be of late Ordovician age, and that the axis of uplift associated with the rising batholith may have been partly responsible for the unconformity. In such a case the transgression would have been more likely to be from south to north (see also Rundle (1979) and the section on intrusions above). Another challenge to previous ideas has been advanced by Branney and Soper (1988). Branney (1988a) has recorded important volcanotectonic structures in the Langdale area (see above) and he and Soper are now of the opinion that these could be widespread across the volcanic outcrop. They suggest that structures previously believed to be pre-Coniston Limestone tectonic folds, including the Ulpha syncline, could now be interpreted as volcanotectonic (Soper, 1987; Soper *et al.*, 1987; Branney, 1988a)

The main phase of the Caledonian Orogeny occurred during the lower Devonian, when there was greenschist facies metamorphism, strong cleavage, polyphase deformation, especially noticeable in the Skiddaw Slates, and important faulting. This can be related to the final episode in the destruction of the Iapetus Ocean with continental collision and the formation of the Old Red Sandstone (Eur-american) Continent (Figure 3).

The fold styles vary a great deal according to lithology both on a large and a small scale. The largely incompetent Skiddaw Slates are deformed in a complex way compared with the highly competent Borrowdale Volcanics, which occur as broad open folds, whereas the Windermere Group contains both incompetent formations with small scale tight folds (Bannisdale Slates), and competent formations with large open structures (Coniston Grits). However, the much larger structure of the Lake District Anticline remains the most important, and all the others are parasitic upon it. The ill-defined axis runs along poorly exposed ground from west of Keswick towards Penrith, the north limb being steeply inclined and the south limb, undulating more gently across the major part of the Lake District. It is predominantly a main phase (Lower Devonian) Caledonian structure (Soper *et al.*, 1987), but is quite likely to have been initiated at an early stage, possibly pre-Borrowdale volcanics (Webb *et al.*, 1987).

The main events of the Caledonian structural history can now be summarised as follows:-

D_0 & D_1 - Slumps and olistostromes affecting the Skiddaw Group.

D_2 - Undivided. The unconformity between the Skiddaw Group and the Borrowdale Volcanic Group (but no recognised minor structures in the former). Volcano-tectonic structures in the Borrowdale volcanics. The Caradoc unconformity between the Borrowdale Volcanic and Windermere Groups.

D_3 - The main Caledonian (Lower Devonian) folding of all the Lower Palaeozoic rocks of the Lake District, with formation of cleavage (formerly D_2).

D_4 - Sideways closing folds best seen in the Skiddaw Slates (formerly D_3).

Details of folding within the three main units are of considerable interest. The overall impression of the Skiddaw Slates is that of highly complex minor folds, especially in the pelites, but much of this is a result of the early small-scale folds, now interpreted as slumps (see above), being subjected to later tectonic folding. Where the slump folds are parallel to the main Caledonian trend they are tightened and can develop an approximate axial planar cleavage, but where they are of different trend the cleavage is oblique to fold axes (Jeans 1972). In the field most of these folds are of small scale with amplitudes of a few metres or less, and are best seen where there are pelite-psammite interbeds. A later phase of folding is of an open recumbent nature, generally with a near horizontal crenulation cleavage, and is restricted to beds which are close to vertical (D_4 above and itineraries 2, 4, 5 and 6).

The highly competent Borrowdale volcanics exhibit folds of an entirely different style from those of the Skiddaw Slates. There are practically no minor folds and the major folds are large scale open structures with half wavelengths of 2 to 7km and limb dips varying from gentle to vertical (Figure 6). The most notable are the Scafell-Place Fell syncline which is easily followed across the whole of the volcanic outcrop (more than 30 km), the Ullswater anticline which brings up Skiddaw Slates in its core, and the Wrynose and Nan Bield anticlines which look as though they should be one structure, but the fold axis cannot be traced across the central Grasmere area (Figure 6). Recently Soper (1987), Soper et al., (1987) and Branney and Soper (1988) have suggested that most of these folds may have volcanotectonic origins. However, it seems to me that their long linear nature is very much like that of the main folds crossing the Windermere Group, and although they may have been initiated at an earlier date, their main period of formation is more likely to have been by compression during the main phase of the Caledonian Orogeny.

Folding of the Windermere Group sediments is different in style again. For 4 or 5 kilometres south-east of the Borrowdale volcanics unconformity the rocks dip steeply to the SE in what is essentially a continuation of the south-east limb of the Wrynose-Nan Bield anticline. Lack of small-scale folding may have been influenced by the large amount of massive greywacke in this part of the sequence and by the underlying Borrowdale volcanics. South of this area the Bannisdale Slates in particular are strongly folded in the form of synclinoria and anticlinoria. The larger folds, with half wavelengths of one or two kilometres, can only be determined by regional mapping and it is not easy to trace them very far, especially since there are no published maps for a large tract west of Windermere (Grizedale Forest). The minor folds, however, are readily appreciated in the field. They have half wavelengths which vary from a few metres to about 200m and are periclinal in form, dying out as conical structures (Webb and Lawrence, 1986; Lawrence et al., 1986). The plunges of the folds are also quite variable across the Lake District. In the east there is a low plunge of less than 5° (Moseley, 1968 and 1972) whereas near Coniston in the west it is about 30° (Soper and Moseley, 1978; Moseley, 1986). It is possible that these variations could be related to the N-S trending disturbances described below.

The nature of the cleavage is also best described under the headings of the three main stratigraphical groups, but aspects common to the whole region are the strike swing from NNE in the south-west to E-W in the east, and the fact that cleavage post-dates Silurian strata.

Within the Skiddaw Slates it is noticeable that intensity varies with lithology and is strong in pelites and weak in psammites. Spaced cleavage predominates and it is unusual to find a truly penetrative fabric. The main cleavage usually dips at a high angle and is frequently parallel to bedding, so that axial planar cleavage is not common, and only seen locally on fold crests. A later, near horizontal crenulation cleavage can often be seen associated with the open recumbent folds (see above).

Cleavage in the Borrowdale volcanics is also related to lithology and is strong in the fine-grained volcaniclastic tuffs, but weak in the more massive lavas and sills. There are also several zones of strong cleavage (high strain) and poor cleavage (low strain) which Firman and Lee (1986) have suggested are related to the roof of the batholith; that is poor, where the batholith is near surface, and strong where it is deeply buried, e.g. on the batholith margins. For example there is a high strain zone with strong cleavage running through Honister, where there are important slate quarries, and yet on the adjacent High Stile range cleavage is almost non-existent.

In the Windermere Group cleavage is again related to lithology and varies from a strong fracture cleavage in pelites to none at all in massive greywacke. Refraction can usually be seen in greywacke graded units, and it is interesting that the strike is a few degrees clockwise of the axial planes of the folds (Moseley, 1968 and 1972; Lawrence et al., 1986; Soper et al., 1987).

Caledonian faulting, like many other structures, developed at various times during the Lower Palaeozoic, with the most important movements associated with the main phase Caledonian Orogeny during the Lower Devonian. It is likely that there was fault activity in pre-Borrowdale times, but it is difficult to prove. Certainly there was much faulting associated with the volcanotectonic movements during Borrowdale volcanic times (Branney, 1988a), and different volcanic successions on opposite sides of the Coniston Fault show that this was active during vulcanicity.

The major faults are, however, related to the cleavage and folding of the main orogeny. North-easterly trending thrusts, north-westerly (dextral) and northerly (sinistral) wrench faults may be expected, and indeed they are present, but there are a number of anomalies of which the most striking example is the N-S Coniston Fault which has a dextral displacement of 1.5 kilometres where it affects the Coniston Limestone. This may reflect an earlier volcanotectonic origin. There are also composite wrench-thrust faults (Figure 6), usually found where a wrench fault passes into an incompetent formation. There are many "bedding" thrusts of this type along the outcrop of the Skelgill shales, and the large Brathay and Coniston Faults are deflected into thrusts along pelitic beds immediately below the massive greywackes of the upper part of the Coldwell and the Coniston Grit Formations (Soper and Moseley, 1978, and Figure 6).

It remains to comment briefly on the relatively mild Hercynian and post-Triassic earth movements. The main effects of Hercynian deformation were in southern Britain and on the Continent. In the Lake District the only recognised phase is the Saalian at the end of the Carboniferous during which there was gentle doming with some sharp monoclinal folds and a moderate amount of faulting. The monoclines are in the east and south-east. Locally they form important N-S structures with vertical west facing limbs, as in the case of the Silverdale disturbance (Figure 7, and Moseley, 1972). The faults mostly have north-westerly and northerly trends. They are normal faults which are posthumous upon Caledonian wrench faults.

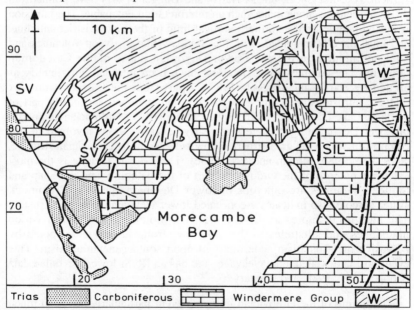

Figure 7. Structure of the southern part of the Lake District. Faults and trend lines are black lines. SV - Skiddaw Slates and Borrowdale Volcanics, C, WH, U, SIL and H are the Cartmel, Whitbarrow, Underbarrow, Silverdale and Hutton Roof disturbances (Moseley, 1972).

During post-Triassic time there was some renewed gentle doming and posthumous movement along the earlier faults (Moseley, 1972). These structures no doubt reflect the tensional regime of the opening Atlantic Ocean.

Intrusions

Igneous intrusions range from large plutonic bodies to small plugs, dykes and sills, and from granite, granodiorite, microgranite and granophyre to diorite, microdiorite, gabbro, dolerite and picrite. Their ages range from early Ordovician to Tertiary (eg. Armathwaite dyke). Of the basic and ultra-basic rocks, those in the north (Carrock, Embleton, Great Cockup) appear to be related to the Eycott Volcanics and those further south (Haweswater Complex) to the Borrowdale Volcanics, although there are exceptions such as the basaltic rocks which cut the Mell Fell Conglomerate.

The Carrock Complex has always been a major attraction for field excursions with its extensive range of igneous rocks from gabbro to granophyre, and the beautifully preserved mafic to felsic cumulate sequences (Hunter and Bowden, itinerary 3). Previously it has been interpreted as a vertical dyke-like sheet, but as Harris and Dagger (1987) have pointed out the field relations alone make such an interpretation untenable. The intrusion is indeed parallel to the northern vertical limb of the Lake District anticline, and must have been folded, with the Skiddaw Slates, Eycott volcanics and later sediments, during the Lower Devonian phase of the Caledonian Orogeny. The complex must therefore have been intruded horizontally as argued by Harris and Dagger (1987). Apart from the Carrock Complex plutonic intrusions of granite composition dominate and are mostly part of the large Lake District batholith (Bott, 1974), partly of Ordovician and partly of lower Devonian age. There are clearly several plutons involved in this complex of which the greater part is now believed to be Ordovician (Rundle, 1979; Lee, 1986, Firman and Lee, 1986). The Eskdale Granite is the most extensive outcrop of the Ordovician part of the batholith, and the Shap and Skiddaw Granites are outcrops of lower Devonian age. The Crummock Water aureole also indicates a concealed lower Devonian granitic intrusion. The aureole occupies an ENE zone 24 kilometres long within which mudstones and siltstones of the Skiddaw Group have been affected by pervasive metasomatism superimposed upon contact metamorphism. This event postdates Caledonian cleavage, and has an Rb/Sr lower Devonian date (Cooper *et al.*, 1988, and itinerary 6).

The timing of the Ordovician intrusive event particularly has been much discussed recently following the paper by Firman and Lee (1986), with their suggestion that it could be related to the late Ordovician (Caradoc) deformation which preceded deposition of the Coniston Limestone. Soper, (1987) and Soper *et al.*, (1987) suggested that the batholith may be genetically related to Borrowdale volcanicity whereas Webb *et al.*, ((1987) think that it was more likely to have been emplaced somewhat later, maybe during the lower Silurian, and Firman and Lee, (1987) finally noted that all was rather speculative and caution should be observed.

Mineralisation

In former times the Lake District was one of Britain's major producers of economic minerals, with the ores of copper, lead, tungsten and iron particularly important. Many other minerals occurred in association with them, and can still be found in mine dumps, whilst cobalt ores, graphite, baryte and related minerals were mined in separate areas. Carrock Mine alone, in addition to the wolframite (tungsten) has recently yielded more than 100 mineral species. There is little mining activity in the region at present and the old mine workings are in a dangerous condition. They should not be entered.

Understandably there has been a great deal written about the mineralisation of the Lake District. The most up to date and comprehensive account is that by Firman (1978a), from which most of this summary has been derived. In addition itineraries 15 and 16 deal with specific mining areas, and mineralisation is also referred to in itineraries 2 and 6. Most of the deposits occur in veins or pipes in the Skiddaw Slates, Borrowdale Volcanics or Carboniferous Limestone, and range in age from late Caledonian (Lower Devonian) to Jurasssic. The earliest are related either to vulcanicity, or more importantly, to the early Devonian intrusive phases of the Lake District Batholith, and the later events, in part still controversial, to the movement of mineralising fluids in connection with minor earth movements. Firman (1978a) has noted that the veins can be classified according to whether they are associated with the main area of the Lake District Batholith, with the steep walls of the Batholith, or have no connection with it at all.

Copper veins are amongst the earliest to have formed, with the more important occurrences having K-Ar dates of 388 Ma (Ineson and Mitchell, 1974), but there are later deposits. During the 19th century more than 50,000 tons of copper were obtained from E-W trending veins associated with ignimbrites and rhyolites in the Borrowdale volcanics (Dagger, 1977; Firman, 1977; Millward and Young, itinerary 15). Copper also occurs in the Newlands Valley, where the E-W veins predate N-S lead veins, in the Wythburn and Thirlspot areas, and further north near Threlkeld and in the Caldbeck Fells.

The wolframite deposits of Carrock Mine are mostly of a similar late Caledonian age, but much younger dates have also been obtained from N-S veins in this area (c 230 Ma).

Lead, with some zinc, is mostly of later date with K-Ar determinations suggesting Namurian to Westphalian ages for the more important deposits (Ineson and Mitchell, 1974). Greenside mine near Ullswater has been the most productive, with N-S veins extending through the Borrowdale volcanics into the Skiddaw Slates, and yielding large tonnages (Gough, 1965).

Hematite is the other important mineral to have been extracted in quantity. It occurs as veins of kidney ore within the Borrowdale volcanics above the granite ridge from Eskdale to Shap ((Davies, 1968; Young, 1984), and in west Cumbria in the Skiddaw Slates and Carboniferous Limestone, where it is found along faults or as replacement deposits along bedding (Carboniferous Limestone only). The much worked pipes of the Millom and Furness areas are nearly all in the Carboniferous Limestone (Rose and Dunham, 1978). They are downward tapering and still have a controversial origin, although it seems probable that iron from the New Red Sandstones has played a part in the formation.

Other minerals of interest are the tourmaline veins around Causey Pike (Cooper *et al.*, 1988) and itinerary 6), the unique veins and nodular masses of graphite of south Borrowdale (Strens, 1965), and barytes in number of Carboniferous Limestone areas.

QUATERNARY

The most striking scenery in the Lake District was produced by glacial erosion during the Quaternary ice ages. There are numerous U-shaped valleys and corries, usually with lakes in the rock basins, and often with morainic dams. Hanging valleys, roches moutonées and glacial striae are common, are easily identified, and are prominent along the routes of many of the itineraries. It is obvious, when considering the Quaternary history of successive glacial and interglacial periods that most of the glacial landforms cannot have been the product of only one glaciation, but must have been formed and extended during several glacial episodes with intervening interglacials giving long periods of normal erosion. In the field, however, it is only the effects of the last, Devensian, ice age (c. 30,000 years BP) which take the eye, and evidence for earlier events has been modified or swept away. Late Glacial activity has also contributed modifications to the glacial landscape, with hummocky moraines at the heads of valleys and on corrie lips, both believed to be Younger Dryas (c. 11,000 years BP) and to correlate with the Loch Lomond Readvance. Other glacial deposits, especially along the main valleys and on lower ground peripheral to the Lake District include spreads of till interlayered with sands and laminated clays, extensive lateral moraines plastered against valley sides, and large areas covered by drumlins. These unconsolidated deposits produce a smooth topography which contrasts strongly with that of the solid rocks, even when the latter are badly exposed.

However, it is not the erosional effects or even the morainic deposits which give the best Quaternary time scales, but sediment deposition in lakes. Unfortunately, as with glacial erosion, evidence for a pre-Devensian history is lacking. The most complete sequence is from the Late Glacial substage of the Devensian (Pennington, 1977 and 1978; Coope and Pennington, 1977), determined from many cores into the sediments of Windermere (the Windermere Interstadial). A sequence of organic silts has yielded plants and insects which indicate a temperate climate prior to the renewed cold of the Younger Dryas, whilst radiocarbon dates have shown that this period extended from c. 14,000 to 11,000 years BP. Other sites yielding organic deposits of the same period include one at Esthwaite Water and there must be others still awaiting discovery.

The Post-Glacial (Flandrian) saw the formation of peat especially in raised bogs. There are extensive deposits along the Kent estuary and in several other mosses such as Foulshaw Moss. Upland blanket peat so extensive on the hills of other parts of northern Britain, was restricted in the Lake District by the steepness of the ground. Solifluction clay, silt, sand and gravel were important during periglacial times and were followed to the present day by hillwash, soil creep and scree formation, and cover lower slopes of many of the valleys. Alluvium was also extensively deposited by the rivers and streams which formed deltas into lakes, some of which have now been entirely silted up.

ITINERARY 1

A geological road map of the Lake District

F. Moseley (After G. H. Mitchell)

Ordnance Survey 1:25,000 Outdoor Leisure Maps 4-7 and 1:50,000 Landranger Series 89, 90, 91, 96 and 97.

I have retained Mitchell's original idea of road routes which traverse the whole region, with stopping points alongside or close to roads. Advantages of an itinerary of this kind are several. For example, during a reconnaissance it can be desirable to see a wide variety of rock formations and structures in a short time, and during bad weather with low cloud and rain it may be unproductive to walk long distances across the fells. Together the localities cover the whole range of Lake District geology. It will be noticed that a number of the stopping points relate to the more detailed itineraries as indicated in Figure 8. The selected routes have been divided into 4 groups, A to D. Since Mitchell's (1970) itinerary some exposures have deteriorated whilst others have become better known. I have checked most of them but cannot profess to have detailed knowledge of every one, whilst Tony Cooper and Dave Millward of the British Geological Survey have checked out localities in the Bassenthwaite, Thornthwaite, Duddon and Eskdale areas. All the routes indicated can be followed by car and minibus, but larger buses will be restricted to the more important main roads.

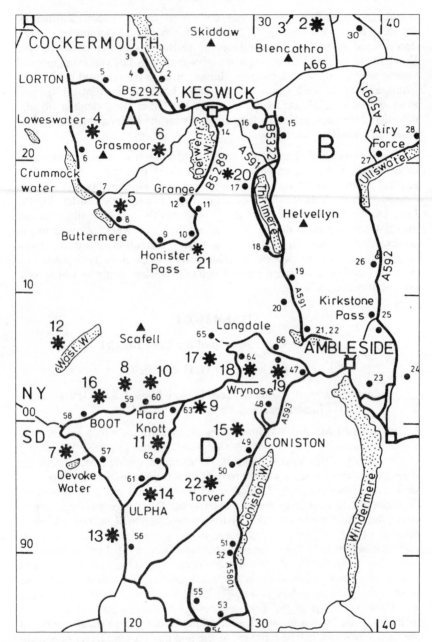

Figure 8. Road route localities in the Lake District, itinerary 1.

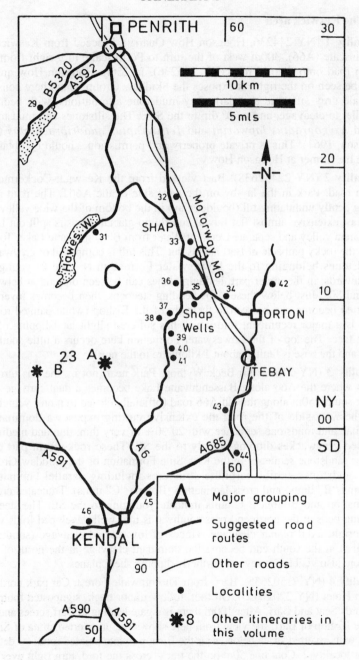

PENRITH

B5320

A592

29

32

SHAP

Hawes W.

31

C

33

Motorway M6

36

35

34

42

ORTON

37

38

Shap
Wells

39

40

41

23 A

B

TEBAY

43

A6

A685

44

A591

45

46

KENDAL

A590

A591

60

30

10 km

5 mls

N

20

10

NY

00

SD

60

90

50

A	Major grouping
	Suggested road routes
	Other roads
●	Localities
✳8	Other itineraries in this volume

A. The Keswick area

Locality 1 (NY 244236, Hodgson How Quarry). Proceed from Keswick to Portinscale (A66). 300m west of the turn to Portinscale, turn right from the main road onto the old road (NY 245236). In 250m Hodgson How quarry will be seen on the right. It exposes the Skiddaw Group which here consists of pale grey siltstone and dark grey mudstone alternations, with bedding parallel to cleavage, and a 60° dip to the SSE. The siltstones and mudstones yield *Azygograptus lapworthi* and *Tetragraptus quadribrachiatus* (see Jackson, 1961). This is private property and permission should be obtained from the farmer at Hodgson How.

Locality 2 (NY 22432638). Barf viewed from the Keswick-Cockermouth main road. Park in the lay-by on the west side of the A66T. The road runs along gently undulating till (boulder clay) in the bottom of the wide valley. To the east extensive almost flat fluvial and fluvio-glacial deposits spill out from the Greta valley and separate Derwent Water from Bassenthwaite Lake. To the west the rocky pinnacle of Barf stands out. This hill is composed of greywacke sandstones belonging to the Loweswater Formation (Figure 2) younging southwards; in the upper part, bedding planes can be seen dipping at between 70 and 80°. Just below these slabs bedding steepens, then becomes inverted; inverted bedding can be seen to the right of the Bishop (white painted rock). Barf is a major recumbent fold which has suffered slight landslipping of its main face. The top of the Loweswater Formation here occurs a little south of Barf and the base is faulted about 1 kilometre to the north.

Locality 3 (NY 21622806) Beck Wythop. Park near, not in, the bus turning point where the A66 along Bassenthwaite Lake becomes a dual carriageway. Walk south 250m along the old A66 road (officially closed to motor vehicles). On the west side of the road the extensive cutting exposes a dominantly siltstone and mudstone sequence with 20-30% of very thin, thin and medium-bedded greywackes dipping steeply to the SE. These rocks form part of a minor sandstone sequence in the Kirk Stile Formation of the Skiddaw Group. The sandstones exhibit turbidite structures including parallel lamination (Bouma "B" units) and cross-lamination (Bouma "C" units). Truncated cross-lamination and Bouma B-C units indicate younging to the SE. The steeply dipping beds at the north end pass southwards into well-developed folds with an upright axial planar cleavage. Traces of low-angled cleavage (southerly dipping) at the south end become the dominant cleavage at the north of the section; also visible are several northerly dipping shear planes.

Locality 4 (NY 21502635). Barf from Thornthwaite Forest. Car park north of Swan Hotel (NY 22052655). On foot, follow minor track, signposted footpath to Lords Seat and Barf. After 100m there is a gate leading to Barf screes and up to the Bishop of Barf; the view from here shows the uninverted strata of Slape Crag with inverted strata below, near the Bishop (white painted rock) — details as for locality 2. Continue 50m on the track, cross the ford, turn right over the stile and take the path uphill parallel to the stream. After 130m notice a small scree to the south which is spoil, with galena and sphalerite, from a mine once situated at the top of the scree. At this height, north of the stream, a flat-topped spoil heap from another adit is visible. Continue uphill and bear left to join the forestry track at around 250m OD (NY 21502635). Walk SE 50-100m and look along strike towards the Bishop. Note the recumbent Barf anticline with slight landslipping along the bedding in Slape Crag and inverted strata with minor folds around and below the Bishop. Along the forestry track here there are small exposures of strongly dipping, uninverted siltstones with subordinate thin cross-laminated (Bouma "C" unit) greywacke beds younging southwards. These are the transitional beds at the top of the Loweswater Formation. If time is available the Bishop of Barf can be visited from the gate at the bottom. The screes have yielded abundant graptolites, but are now nearly barren due to over-collecting; examine the sedimentary structures of the inverted limb around the Bishop. It is a steep dry weather scramble to visit Slape Crag and examine the uninverted limb. Drive south to Braithwaite and take the B5292 to the Whinlatter Pass.

Locality 5 (NY 177258). Scawgill Bridge Quarry exposes extensive beds of quartz-rich greywacke belonging to the Loweswater Formation. Good sedimentery structures, including complete Bouma sequences with basal flute and groove casts, are visible. Bottom structures are best displayed beneath over-hanging ledges in the lower parts of the quarry and indicate their formation by currents derived from the south (Jackson, 1961). The beds are mainly cross-laminated and convolute laminated Bouma "C" units, but there are abundant parallel laminated "B" units and numerous graded "A" units. Interbeds of siltstone and mudstone (Bouma "D" and "F" units) are also common. The sequence is typical of classical medium-grained turbidite sequences as typified by Bouma (1962). It is also a good locality for looking at way-up evidence. This includes bottom structures, graded bedding, the succession of Bouma units in varying combinations; A-B-C-D-E; A-B; C-D etc., truncated cross-lamination and truncated convolute lamination. 100m west of Scawgill bridge (NY 17622571) there is a small roadside quarry in diorite. This is part of an intrusion which extends north-south for about 1.5 kilometres with a width of up to 300m.

Locality 6 From Lorton take the B5289 road to Buttermere. There are excellent views to the east of Whiteside (NY 1722) and Grasmoor (NY 1720). The steep cliffs of Whiteside exhibit complex folds, whilst Grasmoor is within a metamorphic aureole, but it would require a whole day excursion to appreciate these features (see itinerary 4).

Locality 7 (NY 175170). At and near to Buttermere there are several easily accessible and informative exposures (Moseley, 1983, excursion A).

A roche moutonée at Buttermere Church (NY 176170) exhibits polyphase folding in the Buttermere Formation of the Skiddaw Group (Moseley, 1981, figure 146). Buttermere quarry (NY 173172) reveals steeply dipping siltstones and mudstones with load casts on one bedding plane indicating "way up", and just across the road in Long How (NY 172172) the smoothed surfaces of small roches moutonées reveal plunging minor folds in Skiddaw mudstones, which would now be interpreted as slumping of semi-consolidated sediment (F1, see Webb and Cooper 1988 and itineraries 5 and 6).

A short walk (800m) to the south takes one to the bottom of Sour Milk Ghyll (NY 173163), which descends well over 300m (1000 feet) from Bleaberry Tarn, an excellent example of a hanging valley. The ghyll crosses the outcrop of the Ennerdale Granophyre which can be inspected at the edge of the lake (Moseley, 1986, Figures 9 and 11).

Locality 8 Proceed to Honister Pass (NY 22513), with a good view of the hanging valley of Burtness Combe (NY 175145). Itinerary 5 can be reached from Gatescarth (NY 195150). Honister Crag (NY 205142) forms an imposing mass of andesite, basaltic andesite and interbedded volcaniclastic sediment ("bedded tuff") of the Borrowdale Volcanic Group, which rests on Skiddaw Slates. The junction between the two is clearly seen by the change from rough crags to a smoother topography.

Locality 9 (NY 225135). At Honister Pass there is a processing works for Lake District green slate (bedded tuff) which is and has been extensively worked in quarries on both sides of the pass, much of it for export. It is well worth visiting the showroom and shop.

Hopper Quarry (NY 213137), which is a half hour walk uphill from the pass, reveals good evidence for intrusion of a sill into volcaniclastic sediment. The top of the andesite sheet shows extensive development of peperite (Branney and Suthren, 1988).

Locality 10 Follow the road into Borrowdale and to Rosthwaite (NY 259149). The southern part of Borrowdale consists of alluvial flats of former moraine-damned lakes (Raistrick, 1925; Shipp, 1982).

Locality 11 (NY 253264). A mile north of Rosthwaite the Bowder Stone can be seen . It is a large volcanic block, fallen from the crags above. Quayfoot Quarry is nearby (NY 252167) and is formed in gently dipping bedded andesitic tuff with a steep ENE cleavage.

Locality 12 At Grange (NY 255175) there are smooth roche moutonées alongside the river which reveal north trending and steeply dipping Skiddaw mudstones. Nearby at Hollows Farm (NY 247171) there are classic exposures of the Skiddaw Slate-Borrowdale Volcanic junction which have resulted in much controversy as to whether the junction is comfortable or unconformable (Soper, 1970; Mitchell *et al.*, 1972).

Locality 13 (NY 270210) The lower part of the Borrowdale volcanic sequence can be examined in Cat Gill (Ward, 1876; Marr, 1916a; Shackleton, 1966; itinerary 20). There are polygenetic breccias which include andesite, acid volcanics and Skiddaw mudstone, and are interpreted as mudflows. This is the starting point for itinerary 20.

Locality 14 Castle Head (NY 270227). is formed from an intrusive plug of dolerite (Ward, 1876) which may mark the site of a vent for either the Eycott or the Borrowdale volcanics.

B. Keswick-Ambleside-Ullswater

Locality 15. Follow the A66 turning south onto B5322 for St. John's Vale. A number of old quarries show interesting facets of the Threlkeld (St. John's) microgranite (Moseley, 1983). Hilltop quarry (NY 320230), shows unusual recumbent folds in joints. At Bramcrag quarry (NY 320220) the microgranite (dated at 445 Ma, Wadge *et al.*, 1974) is faulted against Skiddaw Slates at the southern margin and overlain by about 10m of sandstone and siltstone which locally form the base of the Borrowdale volcanics. The latter can only be reached by a climbing party (Wadge *et al.*, 1974). Notice the westerly view of High Rigg, with well defined escarpments and benches of lava and tuff dipping 20° south (Moseley, 1972).

Locality 16 (NY 306224). Drive up the narrow (signposted) road to St. John's Church. Here, the lowest part of the volcanic succession and the microgranite with Skiddaw Slate contacts are well seen (Moseley 1983, excursion c). There are excellent views of Blencathra to the north.

Locality 17. Take the road round the west side of Thirlmere (NY 316194). The Armboth dyke of quartz-feldspar porphyry is exposed a few hundred metres up the fellside from the car park at Fisher Gill (NY 305172). Good exposures will be seen at NY 298173, 300157 and 304162, but see Shipp, (1982). Nearby on the lakeshore in Yewhow Wood (308167) there are good exposures of the top of an andesite sill where it intrudes bedded sediments ("tuffs") (Branney and Suthren, 1988).

Locality 18. At NY 317137 adjacent to the road which follows the west side of Thirlmere and the path to Harrop Tarn there is a large glacially smoothed roche moutonée which forms an excellent exposure of gently dipping bedded tuff. It is close to the axis of the Scafell-Place Fell syncline (Hartley, 1941).

Locality 19. Stop in the layby on Dunmail Raise, next to the climbing hut (NY 330110). There is an extensive development of hummocky moraine on the western side of the road, particularly well seen by climbing a little way up the fellside to the east. The first of the small crags on the east side is composed of ignimbritic coarse tuff (breccia) and this is followed by what appears in hand specimen to be flow banded dacite (or rhyolite), but looks more like ignimbrite in thin section. It is part of the Thirlmere "Rhyolite" of Hartley (1941). A traverse of 200m to the north to the first gully reveals undoubted ignimbrite with good eutaxitic texture. To the west of Dunmail Raise the near-horizontally bedded crags of Steel Fell will be seen. These rocks were referred to by Hartley (1941) as Upper "Rhyolites" and Felsitic and Basic Tuffs.

Dunmail Raise and Thirlmere are traversed by the largest fault in the Lake District. It extends from south of Coniston, where there is a strike displacement of more than 1.7km, to beyond the Vale of St. John.

Locality 20. Continue towards Grasmere. Helm Crag to the west (NY 326093) is composed of coarse and bedded tuffs, inclined about 30°N (Moseley, 1986, excursion 8). The escarpments formed by the volcanic units are well seen from the road, but a more complete examination of Helm Crag would require half a day.

Locality 21. Follow the main road past Grasmere to the large quarry (car park) at White Moss (NY 348065, A, Figure 9). The rock here is cleaved unbedded green tuff of medium to fine grain. It is best to drive along the minor road to the top of the hill where there is another car park in an old quarry (NY 345064, B). This is in coarse tuff, the Felsitic and Basic Tuffs of Hartley, (1925), and is now correlated with the Yewdale Breccia (Figure 2). A short walk from here (300m), along a path partly concealed by bracken in summer, will take one to the top of White Moss (NY 345066, C), where there is ignimbritic coarse tuff and breccia. It is very similar to the Yewdale Breccia Formation of Coniston. White Moss is also a magnificent viewpoint for Grasmere, Rydal Water and the surrounding fells.

Locality 22 (NY 349071-352068). The short walk to White Moss can be extended if so desired by continuing north-east to Dunney Beck which meets the path at NY 348069. This will take an extra hour. Alternatively it is possible to drive along the minor road towards Grasmere, turn right at Howe and park at Dunney Beck, after 150m of unmade road. Another route is to follow the well-defined footpath from locality 21A, Figure 9.

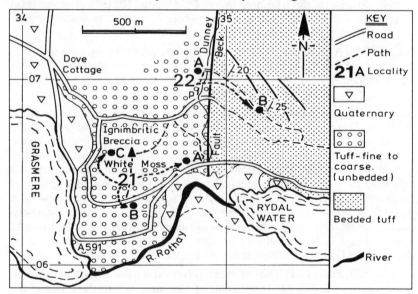

Figure 9. Localities 21A, B, C and 22A, B, along the road route of itinerary 1.

Dunney Beck is an obvious line of a fault separating Hartley's (1925) "felsitic and basic tuffs" from his "bedded tuffs". Take the path up the beck as far as the Thirlmere-Manchester aqueduct at NY 349071 (A), where there is a coarse breccia, probably fault breccia. Notice the palaeomagnetic boreholes into andesite, which appears to be a block in the breccia. Walk east along a path parallel to the aqueduct and after 100m a crag of bedded tuff will be seen just above the path with a dip of 20° south-east. A little further along (NY 352068, B) bedded tuffs descend to the path as a series of small escarpments. They show the intricate sedimentary structures referred to in itinerary 19 and I believe they are part of the upper Tilberthwaite Tuff Formation. A round tour can be completed by following the path to NY 354067 where it descends the fellside near Nab Scar, and another path then leads back to the starting point.

Locality 23 (NY 393029). South of Ambleside and 300m south of Low Wood (NY 387018) tracks lead to High Skelgill Farm, the type locality for the Skelgill Beds. Various species of *Monograptus* and other fossils are common in the stream section. Adjacent to the farm there are exposures of the Applethwaite Beds of the Coniston Limestone Formation (Hutt, 1974-5; Ingham et al., 1978; McNamara, 1979). This is private land and permission should be sought from the farm. Please do not collect unnecessarily.

Locality 24. Continue along the minor road and join the A592 just south of Troutbeck. A large fault follows the valley. On the east side there are quarries in Brathay Flags alongside the Garburn track and just to the north is the type locality for the Applethwaite Member of the Coniston Limestone Formation (NY 426037) (McNamara, 1979; Lawrence et al., 1986). It is a steep 2 kilometres walk from the main road, with the route shown clearly on Outdoor Leisure Map 7.

Locality 25. Stop at Kirkstone Pass (NY 401080). Climb about 20m above the inn on the east side for the view to the west and southwest. The pass itself is covered by a spread of hummocky moraine. About 1 kilometre to the south-west, Pets Quarry will be seen cut into the fellside. Bedded volcaniclastic tuffs are worked, similar to those of locality 22 and probably correlate with the (Upper) Tilberthwaite tuffs. The bedded layers are clearly visible running along the fellside as far as the pass, where they can be inspected in the first outcrop west of the moraine (Moseley, 1983, figure 53). Should one wish to inspect Pets Quarry, permission and a hard hat will be necessary. The bedded deposits are intruded by an andesitic sill, peperitic at its upper margin (Branney and Suthren, 1988).

Locality 26. Pause at the Kirkstonefoot Inn (NY 404119) whence there is an excellent view SW along Dovedale to Dove Crag. The rocks of Dove Crag are tuffs dipping 30° south (Moseley, 1986, figures 47 and 48).

Locality 27. Near Airy Point (NY 402200) there are exposures of microdiorite/dolerite below the road bridge. This is a small intrusion into Skiddaw Slates and probably represents a small Borrowdale volcanic vent. There is a good car park here, and 400m upstream Airy Force can be reached by following a pleasant footpath through the woods. It is a joint controlled waterfall, especially spectacular after rain, and is in andesite.

Locality 28. Continue to NY 436213 and turn left onto the minor road at Knotts for 500m (NY 432217). A path leads to a small quarry where the faulted junction between Skiddaw Slates and Borrowdale volcanics can be seen, although the exposure deteriorates year by year. Above, in another old quarry, there are cleaved coarse tuffs, and a short climb to the top of Birk Crag (NY 430218) takes one to flow-jointed andesite dipping 25° NE (Mitchell *et al.*, 1972; Moseley, 1983, excursion Dd).

Locality 29 (NY 460240). One kilometre before Pooley Bridge there are roadside exposures of the Mell Fell Conglomerate (Devonian) which rises from the road to form the rounded hills of Little and Great Mell Fell (Capewell, 1955; Wadge, 1978).

Locality 30. Should it be the intention to return to the Keswick area, follow the A66 as far as the road to Berrier and Hutton Roof (NY 404278). Turn right (north) as far as the undulating crest of the hill (NY 388306). Here on the west side of the road there is a wide layby adjacent to an old quarry in gently dipping Carboniferous Limestone. There are limestone scars east of the road and Eycott volcanics west of the road (cf. by two barns at NY 388303). There is an obvious feature at the base of the limestones where they rest unconformably on the volcanic rocks. The view south includes the Mell Fells, where there is a great thickness of Devonian conglomerate between the limestone and the Lower Palaeozoic, and the view west and north-west is towards Saddleback and Carrock Fell (itineraries 2 and 3).

A short walk from here takes one to Fairy Knott (NY 384304) where the junction of Skiddaw Slates and Eycott volcanics can be seen (Downie and Soper, 1972) and nearby, to Little Eycott Hill (NY 384301) where the well known porphyritic Eycott basaltic andesite is well exposed (Eastwood *et al.*, 1968).

To return to Keswick by a circular route take a left turn beyond Murrah for Mungrisdale (NY 363306), and then south to the main road (cars and minibuses only).

C. Penrith to Kendal

Locality 31. Take the unclassified road through Askham and Bampton to Hawes Water. At Wallow Crag (NY 495151) there are banded gabbros and banded dolerites (on the crag itself and at the lakeside), forming part of the

Hawes Water dolerite complex, the largest basic intrusive complex of the Lake District and a probable centre for part of the Borrowdale volcanics (Nutt, 1966). On the opposite side of the lake is the hanging valley of Measand Beck.

Locality 32. Follow the road back through Bampton to Shap. 2 kilometres north of Shap Village the prominent Carboniferous Limestone escarpment of Knipe Scar will be seen (NY 530190). There is a large working quarry at 550183, but the best place to examine the limestone is in small disused quarries east of the A6 (NY 558175). The limestones are of Asbian age (*Dibunophyllum* zone of Garwood) (Garwood, 1913 and 1916; Mitchell *et al.*, 1978). See also the Introduction and Figure 5.

Locality 33 (NY 567138). At the southern end of Shap Village the A6 crosses Docker Beck. There is a good section here from the base of the *Seminula gregaria* subzone upwards, with the "algal bed" exposed between the road and the railway, better seen at low water, and the *Thysanophyllum* band below the waterfall 100m beyond the railway (Garwood, 1916). These rocks are of Chadian age (Mitchell *et al.*, 1978). An erratic of Shap Granite will be noticed near the waterfall.

Locality 34 (NY 598092). One kilometre south of Shap Village take the B6261 (NY 567126) for Orton. Roadside quarries expose Chadian limestone with *Thysanophyllum*. The corals are weathered out on joint faces. Please leave them intact. Numerous erratics of Shap Granite resting on limestone will be seen near the road.

Locality 35 (NY 578095). Retrace to the west side of the M6 motorway and take the narrow road to Shap Wells Hotel. West of the hotel on the right bank of Wasdale Beck there are good exposures of Carboniferous Basement Beds, shaly sandstones and conglomerates with pebbles of Shap Granite. They rest unconformably on Brathay Flags (Silurian). Pemission to park at the hotel should be requested.

Locality 36 (NY 565105). Continue from Shap Wells to the A6. 500m north is the Shap Blue Quarry where andesite has been metamorphosed by the Shap Granite. There is much metasomatic mineralisation including epidotisation and the formation of garnet and pyrite veins (Firman, 1954 and 1972). Ask for permission at the adjacent Shap Granite works (NY 567112). I have been told, however, that this quarry is now flooded and disused; enquiries may be necessary, as will a hard hat.

Locality 37. The contact between the Shap Granite and andesite is exposed along the old tramway track (NY 563100).

Locality 38 (NY 556083). The Shap Granite Quarry will be seen on the west of the main road. Three episodes of intrusion are indicated, each stage containing large megacrysts of pink orthoclase. There are also large, dark xenoliths with pink feldspar megacrysts. Many joints have films of pyrite or molybdenite (Grantham, 1928; Firman, 1957 and 1972). A hard hat will be necessary.

Locality 39. A quarry at NY 559078 and roadside cutting at NY 553072 reveal exposures of Brathay Flags and Coldwell Beds, strongly metamorphosed by the Shap Granite.

Locality 40 Park at Shap Summit (NY 554062). A few metres to the south on Red Crag (NY 556059) a red north-westerly trending microgranite dyke will be seen.

Locality 41 (NY 556055). 400m south there is an excellent section in folded Bannisdale Slates; these are slates with greywacke sandstone and siltstone interbeds (Moseley, 1968 and 1986). There are numerous sedimentary structures which one associates with turbidites, and there are the sharp folds typical of the Silurian of the southern Lake District.

An alternative, slightly different route following on from locality 35 is as follows:-

Locality 42. Go east to Orton and to Orton Scar along the Appleby road (B6260). A small quarry on the north side of the road (NY 622095) reveals the *Nematophyllum minus* beds. Please do not remove fossils. Higher up at the top of the bank another quarry (NY 628099), near the base of the Asbian, yields *Alveolites*, and on the top there are extensive outcrops of gently dipping limestone pavement (Garwood, 1916). The Asbian limestones provide the best limestone pavements in the Lake District, for example walk 500m west from the top quarry (above) onto limestone scars (see the Introduction and Figure 5).

Locality 43 (NY 609024). Follow the B6260 from Orton to Tebay and take the A685 for Kendal. There is an excellent section in folded Coniston Grits on Jeffrey's Mount where the road runs parallel to, and west of, the motorway (Moseley, 1972 and 1986).

Locality 44 (SD 613988). There is an old quarry in the Coniston Grit alongside the minor road to Sedbergh.

Locality 45 (SD 542952). Proceed along the A685 for 15 kilometres to Meal Bank. Just west of the railway bridge follow a narrow lane south for 200m, cross the railway bridge and immediately east there is a quarry in Kirby Moor Flags with "ball" structures (concretions) and shell bands (Mitchell, 1970). Unfortunately this quarry is now overgrown and used as a dump. A good but inaccessible section can be seen in the railway cutting from the bridge.

Locality 46. Proceed to Kendal and take the minor road west to Underbarrow. Near the top of the Carboniferous Limestone escarpment there is an old quarry (Scar Quarry) in Holkerian limestone (SD 489924). A short walk along the top of the escarpment to the south yields good views across the Silurian outcrops to the west. The grykes of the limestone pavements (joints) show strong NW orientation. They are parallel to a fault which offsets the escarpment (Scout Scar to Cunswick Scar) by 200 metres (Moseley and Ahmed, 1967).

D. Ambleside, Coniston, Duddon, Eskdale, Langdale

Locality 47 (NY 345035). Take the A593 from Ambleside to Coniston. At Skelwith Bridge there is a showroom and shop for the Lake District green slates. These are mostly from the Tilberthwaite tuffs (itineraries 15 and 19, and localities 25 and 48 this itinerary).

Locality 48 (NY 317014). The large Hodge Close disused quarry is a former source for the green slates (itinerary 19 and Moseley 1983). Turn off the A593 at SD 314998 and proceed for 2 kilometres along a narrow road to the quarry. This is the best exposure of the green slates in the Lake District.

Locality 49. At Coniston take the minor road (Station Road) leading west. At SD 300976 follow the footpath at Dixon Ground Farm to the footbridge across Church Beck at SD 298977. Here there is a good section in graptolitic Skelgill Shales, and upstream a section through the Coniston Limestone. To continue the walk farther follow the path along the south bank of Church Beck to the Miners Bridge (SD 294980), where the route of itinerary 15 will be joined.

Locality 50. At SD 299975 (Coniston) take the narrow steep road. Pass through the fell gate at SD 289971 and continue along the unmade road to Boo Tarn (SD 282968). Here there is an excellent view to the north of the Applethwaite and Longsleddale Formations of the Coniston Limestone which rest on the Borrowdale Volcanics of Timley Knott (itinerary 22 and Moseley, 1983).

Locality 51 (SD 289909). From Coniston continue along the A593 to Torver and take the A5084. At SD 289909 there is a disused quarry with a beautifully exposed 10m wide microgranite dyke. It was intruded into Bannisdale Slates (sandy siltstone) which exhibit a variety of sedimentary structures (Moseley, 1986).

Locality 52. At SD 287901 there is a good layby, and nearby on the roadside, several sharp folds in mudstone and in massive greywacke. Walk 300m along the footpath towards Beacon Tarn and several folds will be seen. The rocks are part of the Bannisdale Slate Formation and the folds plunge 20-30 degrees north-east.

Locality 53 (SD 280854). Take the minor road from Lowick Bridge and turn right onto the A5092. At SD 280854 on the north side of a small stretch of dual carriageway there is a cutting in Coniston Grit, with a wide variety of sedimentary structures (loads, grooves, grading etc.).

Locality 54 (SD 268847). Brathay Flags can be inspected in the abandoned Gawthwaite Quarries. Mudstone and siltstone laminae intersect the cleavage at a high angle.

Locality 55 (SD 256858). Take a minor road leading north-west at SD 262849. The hill at Burney shows excellent flute casts in Coniston Grit on the crag on the north side of the road, adjacent to the house. Further on there are sole and other structures in greywacke units.

Locality 56 (SD 202912). Continue along the A595, Millom Road, through Broughton-in-Furness and just before Duddon Bridge (SD 19958820) turn right for Ulpha. The prominent escarpment to the north-east is formed of Borrowdale Volcanic rocks. A pleasant view northwards along the Duddon Valley can be seen from Stonestar. The stream entering the valley from the south-east is along a prominent glacial meltwater channel. The blocky flow-brecciated top of an andesite flow is exposed on the west side of the road.

Cross the River Duddon at Ulpha and, after 700m, the road to Eskdale and route (a) of this itinerary is to the left. For those who do not wish to attempt Hard Knott Pass (1 in 3 gradients and many tight bends) route (b) continues along the valley road via Hall Dunnerdale to rejoin the main excursion at Cockley Beck (NY 24660165). At this point, therefore, there are two routes, (a) and (b).

(a) Eskdale and Hard Knott

Locality 57. After climbing out of the Duddon Valley, the road crosses an undulating peat and boulder clay covered plateau. At SD 17629716 there is a spectacular view of the Scafell Range. The white weathered rocks on the north side of Eskdale are outcrops of the granite. A further 750m along this road is the crossroads with a track west leading to Devoke Water. Itinerary 7 begins from this cross-roads.

Locality 58 (SD 161993). Continue to Eskdale, noting on the descent the straight, fault-guided valley of Whis Gill. The crags in this area are of well-jointed coarse-grained granite. After crossing Forge Bridge turn right at the public house in the direction of Boot. Dalegarth Station (NY 17340071) is the start of itinerary 16. Hereabouts there are good views of the scenery in Eskdale.

Locality 59 (NY 189098). About 1.3 kilometres east of Boot, near the Woolpack Inn is a small lane on the south side of the road that leads to Doctor Bridge. Coarse-grained granite, cut by a lamprophyre dyke, is exposed in the stream.

Locality 60. Proceed eastwards to Hard Knott Pass where the Roman Fort (NY 218015) may be visited. The contact between the granite and volcanic rocks is exposed west of the Esk in the low hills above Taw House. The crags of Border End to the north of the pass expose porphyritic andesite lavas with thin interbedded tuffs giving rise to prominent 'trap topography'. Details of the geology of this area are to be found in itinerary 10.

Continue over the Pass to Cockley Beck.

(b) Duddon Valley (Alternative route from locality 56, avoiding Hard Knott Pass).

Locality 61 (SD 213953). Continue along the valley to the bridge near Hall Dunnerdale where the scenic view of the valley and Wallowbarrow Crag will be appreciated.

Locality 62 (SD 22909718). After crossing Tarn Beck the car may be parked near the cattle grid north of Hollin House Tongue. This prominent knoll has good exposures of parallel bedded, andesitic coarse tuff with normal and reverse grading, and in which channels are present. Drive north and join the main route at Cockley Beck.

Locality 63 (NY 246017). At Cockley Beck Bridge park the car and on foot follow the enclosure wall on the north-west side of the river for about 300m. Hereabouts are good exposures of a garnet-bearing eutaxitic ignimbrite. Note the size grading of the large fiamme in this unit and also the thin interbeds of garnet-bearing coarse tuff with low-angle cross-stratification. This prominent marker horizon is further seen on itineraries 9 and 10, the former starting from Cockley Beck.

Continue by road along the upper part of the Duddon Valley to the Wrynose Pass, noting the large grass covered alluvial fans draining from Gaitscale Gill to the north. Should time be available a short walk of three kilometres from the Three Shires Stone (NY 277027, parking for cars and minibuses) will take one to Little Stand (NY 251031) and Cold Pike (NY 264035). Here there are beautifully exposed flow folds in an andesite sheet which was interpreted as a lava by Allen *et al* (1987), but, because of the peperitic upper margin, as a sill by Branney and Suthren (1988). Note that itinerary 17 starts from Wrynose Pass.

Locality 64. Descend from Wrynose Pass into Little Langdale and take the narrow road to Great Langdale at NY 302033. Observe Blea Tarn and stop at the col and the Langdale Pikes overlook (NY 289052). The Langdale Pike stratigraphical sequence from the Old Dungeon Ghyll Hotel upwards consists of dacite, ignimbrite, various bedded tuffs and breccia, dacite, ignimbrite and, at the top of the Pikes, the Tilberthwaite (Seathwaite Fells) tuff (Moseley, 1983 figures 60 and 62). The view south reveals a prominent straight gully rising behind Bleatarn House (NY 295048). This is the line of an important shatter zone which extends from Little Langdale across the col and into Rossett Gill (NY 250074). The col is also the starting point for the Side Pike itinerary 18.

Locality 65. Proceed into Great Langdale and the car park at the hotel (NY 285061). A footpath leads west on the north side of the beck. Good examples of dacite, ignimbrite and bedded tuff from the sequence mentioned under locality 64, can be seen in the screes which descend to the path. Two kilometres from the hotel in Mickleden (NY 265070) there is a large area of late-glacial moraine.

Locality 66 (NY 316056). Proceed down Great Langdale to Thrang (Chapel Stile) where the Tilberthwaite Tuffs with a wide variety of sedimentary structures are exposed in the old quarries (see itinerary 19). Return to Ambleside by the B5343 and A593.

ITINERARY 2

Mungrisdale and the Caldew Valley

D. E. Roberts, Bristol University

1:25,000 map NY 33.

The essential purpose of this excursion is to examine Skiddaw Slates, some of which are within the aureole of the Skiddaw Granite. The main features of interest are the various deformation phases of the Caledonian Orogeny which are well-displayed at Raven Crags, Mungrisdale and in the area from the River Caldew along Ling Thrang Crags to Tarn Crags on Bowscale Fell. The nature of the Skiddaw Granite aureole can also be noted with a progression from chlorite overgrowths at the margin to cordierite hornfels or andalusite hornfels in the inner zone, the different mineral assemblages being dependent on initial rock composition. The Grainsgill outcrop of the Skiddaw Granite will also be included and localities where the alteration to greisen can be seen will be indicated. The tungsten-bearing veins at Carrock Mine which occur within both the greisen and hornfelsed Skiddaw slates conclude the itinerary (Figure 10).

Three major lithological divisions of the Skiddaw Slates are recognisable in the area, namely interbedded greywackes and slates (Loweswater Flags); interbedded slates and siltstones with thin sandstones, and black slates (lower and upper divisions of the Kirkstile Slates) (Roberts, 1977a). Four deformation phases have been recognised in the Skiddaw Slates for this area (Roberts, 1977a) and of these the last three represent different pulses of the Caledonian Orogeny. The first phase, however, may not have the tectonic connections that it was once believed to have, but is certainly much earlier than the others (see the Introduction). The D_1 structures are tight recumbent folds with a very steep plunge of variable trend and are best seen in the metamorphosed lower interbedded slates and siltstone division of the

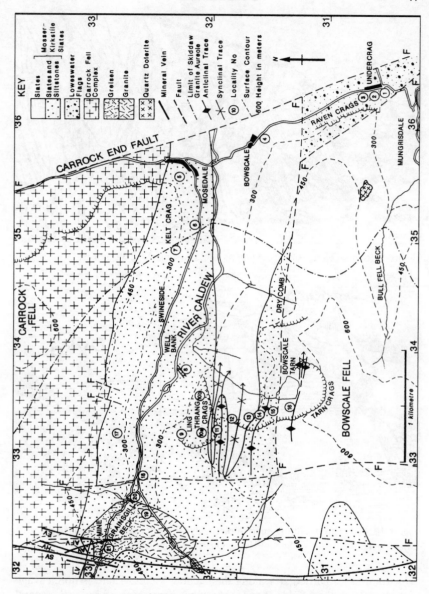

Figure 10. Map of the Mungrisdale-Caldew Valley area showing the main geological boundaries and the localities mentioned in the text. Abbreviations for the mineralised veins at Carrock Mine: EV - Emmerson Vein, AFV - Ankerite Fault Vein, AV - Ankerite Vein, HV - Harding Vein, SV - Smith Vein, LV - Lead Vein.

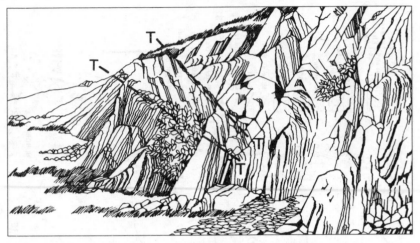

Figure 11. School House Quarry, Mungrisdale, showing the E-W thrusts.

Figure 12. D5 fractures cutting quartz-dolerite dykes, with associated folds in the adjacent slates at E end of School House Quarry, Mungrisdale.

Kirkstile Slates, particularly along the Caldew Valley. There is no cleavage associated with these folds. The D_2 phase has been reserved for such general Lake District events as the initiation of the main Lake District Anticline and various volcano-tectonic and Caradoc structures which are not represented in this area (see the Introduction). The D_3 structures are upright open folds with a strong associated slaty cleavage in the slates, and have the NE-SW trend typical of the Caledonian structures. D_4 structures are sideways closing minor folds with a sub-horizontal axial planar and crenulation cleavage. Their orientation is essentially NE-SW due to their having formed on the steep limbs of the larger and dominant D_3 folds. D_5 structures are minor N-S open folds with a strong associated steep fracture cleavage and with a plunge either to the N or S being dependent on the attitude of the major structure on which they have developed.

Locality 1 (NY 363305). A good place to start an examination of this area (and to leave any vehicles) is School-House Quarry, Mungrisdale. Here black slates dipping steeply to the south occur with a weak S_2, E-W cleavage sub-parallel to the bedding. From the eastern end of the quarry looking westwards two gently inclined E-W thrusts with associated sub-horizontal folds can be seen to dominate the structure (Figure 11). A faint crenulation parallel to the thrust and with a gentle easterly plunge is also visible on bedding planes over most of the quarry. These are all D_4 structures and the thrusts are most likely to be accommodation structures for stresses acting during the formation of the D_4 folds. At the eastern end of the quarry two highly altered quartz-dolerite dykes occur parallel to the bedding and are visible both in the side wall and in the quarry floor where they have been displaced along minor north-south faults. Steeply plunging north-south minor folds, with a steeply inclined associated fracture cleavage occur in the slates adjacent to the dykes along the lines of the faults and these are regarded as being D_5 structures (Figure 12). The dykes reacted to the D_5 stresses by brittle fracture whereas the more ductile slates accommodated the stresses by folding and the development of the fracture cleavage.

The slates in Mungrisdale Quarry have yielded a *Didymograptus deflexus* fauna which Jackson (1961) placed at the base of the Loweswater Flags, though he did classify the rocks on lithological grounds as the Hope Beck Slates (see Figure 2), which he regarded as being unfossiliferous.

Locality 2 (NY 363306). The exposures on Raven Crags form a northern continuation of those in Mungrisdale Quarry for approximately 500m. The crags themselves comprise a set of steeply inclined exposures separated by relatively flat unexposed ground. A number of prominent hollows more or less perpendicular to the crags themselves represent the lines of faults or master joints. The rocks are Loweswater Flags, and throughout the exposures on the crags small scale sedimentary structures are clearly visible on weathered surfaces in the more arenaceous beds. These include current, convolute and graded bedding with some flute casts, the overall succession being indicative of a turbidite sequence.

The structure of Raven Crags has been discussed in detail by Roberts, (1977b) who also produced a detailed map of the crags. The structures described in that paper can easily be detected in the field with reference to the map. This and other published maps of this area are unfortunately too large and detailed to be reproduced here. The crags have been divided into a southern section where the structure follows the regional E-W trend approximately 100m N of Mungrisdale Quarry, and a northern section where asymmetric folds with a gentle WSW limb and a steep ENE limb have an anomalous NW trend. Immediately to the north-west of Mungrisdale Quarry D_3 structures dominate with a strong overprint of D_4. D_1 structures are not common and although they follow the D_3 trend, can be distinguished from them by their steep plunge. D_5 structures are also uncommon.

Locality 3 (NY 363307). Proceeding northwards the folds with a NW-SE trend can be noted 100m to the west and 100m to the north-west of the northeastern end of Undercrag Farm at the base of the crags. Here, near a prominent syncline, occur minor folds with similar conjugate and concentric fold elements. Also clearly displayed is an associated cleavage which approximates to a true slaty cleavage in the pelites, but with accompanying cleavage refraction becomes a spaced cleavage in the psammites. These structures are typical of the crags and serve as a convenient locality to study them, but, of course, a more extensive examination would reveal the overall structure. A good way to achieve this briefly is to make an east to west traverse of the crags from Locality 3 (Figure 13). With reference to the map produced by Roberts, (1977b, figure 2) this is along section line D-C and a return to the base of the crags could be made along the line of Section A-D. D_1 folds are not easily detected in this section; D_4 folds are rare mainly because of the dominantly gentle dip of the strata. D_5 structures are absent.

Locality 4 (NY 360315). North towards Bowscale the crags end (NY 360311) and a continuation along this direction onto the low exposures at Bowscale reveals a change in rock type to black slate — the upper slaty division of the Kirkstile Slates. It is likely that a fault occurs in the hollow

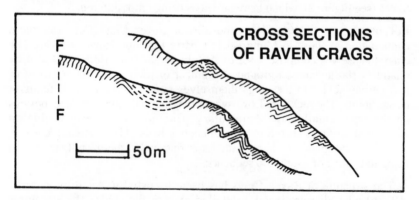

CROSS SECTIONS OF RAVEN CRAGS

50m

Figure 13. Cross section of D3 folds at Raven Crags (after Roberts, 1977b, Fig. 2).

now occupied by two small streams and separates the two rock types. At Bowscale the most common structures visible are D_4 minor folds with a microfold crenulation cleavage and D_4 minor folds associated crenulation/spaced cleavage. This is a good locality to see the relative ages of D_4 and D_5 structures with the D_4 cleavage cutting across the D_4 microcrenulations.

A point worthy of note here is how abruptly Bowscale Fell and Carrock Fell are terminated to the east by a series of crags including Raven Crags. The low ground to the east is drift-covered but boreholes have proved Skiddaw Slates at depth. A large fault, the Carrock End fault is postulated to occur along this line and Moseley (1972) projects its continuation as far south as Ullswater.

Locality 5 (NY 356323). If vehicles have been left at Mungrisdale, return to them and then drive to the Caldew Valley. A possible short detour, though not critical to the understanding of the area, is to visit the crags at the bottom of Carrock Fell above Mosedale. Here steeply plunging D_1 folds occur in psammites which have been metamorphosed by the intrusion of the Carrock Fell Complex.

Locality 6 (NY 351321). Continue to the top of the small hill on the road. Here it is possible to see some of the geomorphological features resulting from the Pleistocene glaciation. The small hill itself is actually the remains of a morainic barrier which dammed a post-glacial lake extending as far up the valley as Swineside (NY 339330) and the flat valley floor is covered by lacustrine sediments. During the 1960s some test drilling was carried out at this point with a view to considering the site as a potential reservoir.

Locality 7 (NY 349323). Another short, though not critical detour, could be made to Kelt Crag. Here the psammites of the Kirkstile Slates display small spots of chlorite. They indicate the limit of the Skiddaw Granite Aureole and are superimposed on the heating effects of the Carrock Fell Complex.

Localities 8 to 16 (NY 338323 to NY 335314). The next area which should receive some attention is Ling Thrang Crags and Bowscale Tarn Crags. These are best studied by way of a traverse from the N end of Ling Thrang Crags (NY 332323) southwards to Tarn Crags (NY 336310), and the easiest approach is across the River Caldew via the footbridge at Swineside. A map of these crags has been published (Roberts, 1977a) and reference to it would aid any visit to the area.

Approximately 100m to the west of the bridge a small quartz dolerite dyke occurs within a biotite cordierite hornfels (Loc 8, NY 338323). The parent rock of the hornfels was the siltstone and slates division of the Kirkstile Slates and even in its metamorphosed state is obviously a distinct lithology from the Loweswater Flags displayed on Raven Crags or the black slates at Bowscale. It is now a hard, black, banded hornfels with clear black spots of cordierite when fresh, but when weathered is a dull brown with the bands clearly picked out. Most of the boulders strewn over the valley bottom are also of this lithology.

Proceed to the N end of Ling Thrang Crags (Locality, NY 332323) where large, good exposures of cordierite hornfels occur. Displayed in these rocks are some very good examples of D_1 folds, some of which are tight and angular (Figure 14) whereas others are more irregular. However, in all cases the plunge of these folds is steep and this helps to distinguish them from D_3 structures. The D_1 structures seem to be restricted to the N end of the crags and ironically some of the more complex fold patterns occur in the loose

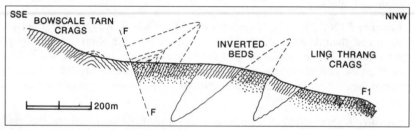

Figure 14. Cross section of Ling Thrang Crags and Bowscale Tarn Crags, showing D_3 overfolds (after Roberts, 1977a).

blocks. Continue an upwards traverse of the crags to the south and to the east where a reduction in metamorphic grade will be noticed, the hornfels gradually becoming a cordierite slate. It is possible in the slates and siltstones to see sedimentary structures and a close examination of these is recommended in order to detect younging directions. Also, this is one of the best areas to see D_4 structures (Figure 15) both folds and sub-horizontal crenulation cleavage (Localities 10a, NY 333321 and 10b, NY 336321). Thin-sections of specimens taken from this locality show that the cordierite has statically overgrown the main cleavage S_3, but that the S_4 crenulations are refracted around them, giving the timing of the cordierite growth as between D_3 and D_4. Towards the top of Ling Thrang Crags (Locality 11, NY333320) the siltstone bands become fewer and the rock type is essentially a slate. At the top of the crags however, siltstones and slates re-appear and here an examination of the sedimentary structures will show that the beds are overturned revealing that the slates are in the core of an overfold. Continue southwards over the unexposed ground to the small crags just before the main area of Bowscale Tarn Crags (Locality 12, NY334318). Here there is an exposure of southerly dipping slate, but the contact with the siltstones and sandstones is not exposed. At the northern end of the main area of Bowscale Tarn Crags a contact between the slates and a bedded unit of slates, siltstones and sandstones can be detected (Locality 13, NY334317). Continue the

Figure 15. Minor D1 folds in cordierite slate at the E end of Ling Thrang Crags.

traverse to the south checking the younging direction in the southerly dipping rocks until a large, close overfold can be seen (Locality 14, NY 334316). The presence of this structure confirms that the repetition of slates and slates with siltstones and sandstones is due to large-scale, northerly facing overfolds. Approximately 100m to the south the bedded unit is brought into contact with blue-grey cordierite-andalusite hornfels by a fault (Locality 15, 335315), which is quite likely to be the same structure that separates the Loweswater Flags on Raven Crags from the black slates at Bowscale. The crags at the back of Bowscale Tarn are entirely composed of cordierite andalusite hornfels which is metamorphosed black slate of the Kirkstile Slate Formation which displays a much simpler structure than do the slates of Ling Thrang Crags. For the most part they dip at a moderate degree to the south with some minor D_3 folds, but this pattern is interrupted by a large open E-W upright anticline which can be determined by change in dip and strike just over 100m to the south of the fault (Locality 16, NY 335314). The moraine dammed lake of Bowscale Tarn is worthy of note as is the morainic debris below it on the fell side. Return to Swineside and travel for approximately 1 kilometre up the valley, noting the large boulders of hornfels on the fell sides, until solid rocks form the bed of the River Caldew (NY 33103260).

Locality 17 (NY 33303275). A useful detour for the fit and keen would be to the crags on the flanks of Carrock Fell. Some magnificent D_1 structures are displayed in these hornfelsed siltstones as well as some close N-S joints which could be relict S5.

Locality 18 (NY 331326 to NY 328326). The bed of the River Caldew, from a small dam for approximately 450m upstream, displays a magnificent section of folded hornfelsed Skiddaw Slates which are best examined when the level of the River Caldew is low since many good exposures are covered by water when the level is high. The section has been described together with a detailed map by Roberts (1971). For 250m upstream of the dam the rock is a biotite cordierite hornfels but at a position where a small stream enters the river from the north the lithology changes abruptly to a lighter coloured quartz muscovite hornfels with chlorite pseudomorphing the cordierite. The quartz-muscovite-chlorite hornfels is the lithology exposed as far as the granite and greisen outcrops in the River Caldew and Grainsgill Beck respectively. It is likely that a fault with a downthrow to the east separates the two lithologies though there is little other evidence for its presence in the river itself.

The style of folds in the section is complex with frequently more than one style being present in a single fold. An examination of the exposures along the section will show concentric, similar, chevron and conjugate fold elements, though close to tight similar folds are the most dominant style. Refold interference patterns can also be detected, a good hook type being visible at the junction of Grainsgill Beck. One common feature of many structures is disharmony of fold wavelength in the core of the folds together with discordant structures. There is no obvious orientation of the structures though overall a generalized NE-SW trend can be detected. What is obvious,

Figure 16. D$_1$ folds in cordierite-biotite hornfels in N bank of the River Caldew.

however, is the steep plunge of the folds over the entire section, with only a few exceptions. Roberts (1971) removed a regional dip from these structures and showed that many were originally of N-S recumbent attitude. It would not be practical to describe all the individual exposures here but a prominent set of folds near the road approximately 200m west of the dam (Figure 16), exposures, each side of a small waterfall 30m west of the small tributary, and those 50m upstream of the confluence of Grainsgill Beck, would indicate the overall nature of the area for those who do not wish to examine the entire section in detail.

The origin and timing of these folds is not clear cut and I have revised my own interpretation since they were first described. The steeply plunging folds are still regarded as D_1 structures and it is likely that they were originally recumbent as previously interpreted. However, since the publication of the original paper (Roberts, 1971) the nature and intensity of Caradoc deformation in the Lake District has been shown to be less significant than formerly accepted (Soper and Numan, 1974) and consequently a Caradoc tectonic event is unlikely to be the cause of the D_1 folds in the Caldew Valley. The steep plunge and variable orientation precludes them from being part of the main Acadian deformation, though as a result of thermal metamorphism no Acadian cleavage cutting the folds can be detected. The refolds are likely to be the effect of the Acadian deformation (D_3) on D_1 folds. A close examination of the folds in the section reveals much disharmonic folding, disruption in the hinge zone, apparent shears and some irregular convolute folds not dissimilar from features produced as a result of slump folding of unconsolidated sediments. This, together with the original recumbent attitude, would point to gravity sliding of unconsolidated material as a more likely mechanism for the formation of the D_1 folds in the Caldew Valley as suggested by Roberts (1977a). The tight nature of some folds with angular hinges is likely to be the result of the recumbent folds having been flattened by the main end-Silurian tectonic event. It is not at all easy to put an undisputable age to the formation of the D_1 folds but regional evidence would point to instability during the onset of Llanvirn of Llandeilo volcanism as being the most likely cause. Since Llanvirn volcanic rocks occur to the north of Carrock Fell, this is the favoured time for the formation of the folds and the proximity of those rocks may be the reason why D_1 folds are so prolific in the Caldew Valley.

Locality 19 (NY 325325). After examining the folds, proceed along the River Caldew until some small exposures of granite occur in the bed of the river. This is the granitic (rather than greisen) part of the Grainsgill or northern outcrop of the Skiddaw Granite. It is essentially composed of feldspar, quartz and biotite though the feldspars indicate some alteration to sericite.

Locality 20 (NY 327327). Return to the confluence of Grainsgill Beck with the River Caldew and examine the 100m of section between the confluence and the small bridge. The downstream half of the section is in relatively unfolded muscovite chlorite hornfels, but some significant changes occur over the last 60m or so towards the bridge and an account of the field relationships and chemical analysis has been published (Roberts, 1983). Below the bridge a sharp contact of the hornfelsed slate and the Grainsgill Greisen can be seen, with the dip of the contact being approximately 10°. The greisen is composed of quartz, and muscovite which occurs as both alteration of feldspar and replacement of biotite. This is the altered northern part of the Grainsgill outcrop of the Skiddaw Granite. The contact of the Greisen with the hornfels can be traced for approximately 50m downstream of the bridge on the SW bank and a small mass of greisen occurs along joints in the hornfels in the stream bed approximately 20m further downstream (Roberts, 1983, figure 2). This demonstrates the irregular nature of the roof of the Grainsgill Greisen. Metasomatic alteration of the hornfels occurs for approximately 15m from the margin of the greisen, the hornfels now being composed of quartz and muscovite, both as a mica mat and as a replacement for biotite. The transition from a dark biotite-bearing rock to a lighter muscovite-rich rock is sharp and easily noted in the field. The zone of alteration is oblique to the original sedimentary bands which are still visible in both rock types. Within this altered zone porphyroblasts of chlorite pseudomorphing cordierite are rare.

Chemical analyses have shown that the greisen was produced by the liberation of K and Na from the granite by hydrothermal fluids. The liberated K in the hydrothermal fluids gave rise to the metasomatism of the adjacent hornfels and also to the retrogressive metamorphism of the biotite cordierite hornfels to the chlorite-muscovite hornfels for a radius of up to 200m from the intrusion. This feature is classical wall rock alteration of the potassic type and indicates potential for mineral deposits.

Locality 21 (NY 332329). The potential has been realised in this area in the well known quartz-tungsten veins at Carrock Mine, which has been working intermittently in recent years and which can be reached by a short walk of approximately 200m upstream along Grainsgill Beck where some exposures of the greisen can be seen, or along the mine road. The veins have been described by Hitchen (1934) and a more recent discussion on their genesis by Shepherd et al., (1976). The veins are N-S vertical structures cutting through the greisen and hornfelsed Skiddaw Slate but dying out northwards as the gabbros of Carrock Fell are encountered. They are tungsten-bearing only adjacent to the area of wall rock alteration, the southerly continuation being barren quartz. The best exposures of the veins are within the mine but surface workings are still obvious on both Coomb Height and the flanks of Carrock Fell. Miners' footpaths can be seen on Coomb Height and it is from one of these above the remains of the Old Compressor House that the best impression of the veins can be gained. The main adit leads into the Harding Vein which can be seen on the flanks of Carrock Fell some 50m to the west of Brandy Gill where some of the underground workings reached surface. Some wolframite can still be seen in the vein here though access to the mine at this point would be highly dangerous. The easternmost vein, the Emmerson Vein, also had extensive surface workings which are present as deep trenches. Between these two veins are the Ankerite Vein and the Ankerite Fault Vein, the former being visible some 200m up Brandy Gill from its junction with Grainsgill Beck. To the west of the Harding Vein is the Mith Vein, the position of which can be noted by the presence of an old level. A poorly exposed E-W fault-controlled quartz-carbonate-sulphide vein, the Lead Vein, cuts the Smith & Harding Veins approximately 75m to the north of Grainsgill Beck.

With the permission of the owners of the mine and the company of an experienced mine geologist it may be possible to visit the underground workings to note the distribution of minerals within the veins. However, despite their having been picked over by generations of geologists and mineral collectors, it is still possible to find some of the many minerals which occur in the veins on the mine dumps. These include wolframite, scheelite, arsenopyrite, chalcopyrite, molybdenite, marmatite, ankerite, dark green apatite, and dolomite. A search for these is normally rewarding and provides some useful relaxation to conclude the day.

ITINERARY 3

The Carrock Fell Igneous Complex

Robert H. Hunter and Neil Bowden
University of Liverpool

1:25,000 map NY33

The Carrock Fell Complex is a multiple intrusion, of dyke-like form, approximately 18 km^2 in size. It was formed during two phases of igneous activity which produced the Mosedale gabbros at 468±10 Ma (K/Ar) and the Carrock gabbro-granophyre complex at 416±20 Ma (Rb/Sr) (Rundle, 1979). These two major units are now given the names Mosedale series and Carrock series respectively; the terms do not have any chronostratigraphical implications. It should be noted that the Mosedale series is equivalent to the Carrock Fell Gabbro of previous works. (eg. the classic papers of Harker, 1894, 1895; Eastwood et al., 1968).

The two series are chemically and mineralogically distinct; the earlier intrusions are genetically related to the Eycott Volcanic Group and the later ones represent a distinct suite of rocks related by fractional crystallisation of a tholeiitic basalt in a continental margin extensional or transtensional tectonic regime (Hunter, 1980).

The Mosedale series layered rocks are ortho- and mesocumulate gabbros which accumulated or crystallised *in situ* on an inclined floor of a periodically replenished, dyke-like magma chamber. Many of the classic features of small to medium-sized layered gabbroic intrusions are displayed, e.g., modal layering, mineral lamination, cryptic variation. Several distinct mappable units are present (Figures 17 and 19), which broadly correspond with the units defined by Eastwood *et al.*, (1968), these have been redefined, in part, to conform to current layered intrusion nomenclature (e.g., Irvine, 1982). The southern contact is against Skiddaw Slates, the western and eastern contacts are faulted and the northern contact is against the later Carrock series. A significant portion of the layered gabbroic intrusion may have been removed (down-faulted) during the emplacement of the Carrock series.

The Carrock series forms the northern half of the outcrop of the Complex. Its eastern, northern and western contacts are faulted against the Eycott Volcanics and the Drygill Shales/Harestones felsite. It is composed of three units: the granophyres of Carrock Fell and Rae Crags and the gabbro of Round Knott and Miton Hill (the 'diabase' of earlier authors). The granophyres were part of a single body which was bisected by the emplacement of the gabbro. The granophyre is thought to represent the subsided roof-zone of a zoned tholeiitic magma chamber. At deeper levels in the magma chamber (the present erosion level), crystallisation along sub-vertical walls, from magmas evolving along a Fe-andesite (icelandite)-dacite-rhyolite liquid line of descent, resulted in formation of iron-rich gabbroic, dioritic and monzodioritic orthocumulates which now form the Marginal Zone. Residual trapped melt in these side-wall cumulates crystallised as interstitial, granophyric intergrowths. This side-wall crystallisation may have been from buoyant boundary-layer flows which were feeding the evolved, rhyolitic roof zone. Crystallisation of the roof zone produced by granophyre. During a period of subsequent roof subsidence (perhaps coupled with an eruption), crystal-rich rhyolite was emplaced as a sub-vertical sheet into the Marginal Zone where it crystallised to form porphyritic granophyre. Less evolved basaltic magma from deeper in the chamber was emplaced as a dyke-like body further north into the granophyre where it differentiated in situ to form the Gabbro Unit. The heat from crystallisation of the Carrock Magma chamber produced a hydrothermal convective system which altered the northern Mosedale series gabbros and also the early-formed rocks of the Marginal Zone resulting in formation of transgressive and replacement pegmatites. The western portion of the Complex was subsequently metamorphosed and altered by the effects of the Skiddaw Granite and Brandy Gill mineralisation. Former interpretation of intermediate rocks in the Further Gill Syke area at the contact between the two units, as a mixed hybrid origin (Harker, 1894, 1895; Eastwood et al., 1968) is not supported by the evidence either from chemistry and mineralogy or from radiometric dating.

The purpose of the itinerary is two fold: (a) to examine contact relationships, structural and mineralogical features of the Mosedale series gabbros in a traverse which moves stratigraphically up the layered sequence (localities 1-9); and (b) to examine the mineralogical and structural features of the Marginal Zone of the Carrock series (localities 10-15). An extension of the itinerary (localities A-D) has been included to encompass an ascent of Carrock Fell (660m). The itinerary from 1 to 15 would provide plenty of time for examining the field relationships and for discussion and would provide a reasonably leisurely day outing: the Mosedale series before lunch and the Carrock series after. It is, of course, possible to start in Further Gill Sike and do the itinerary in reverse. However, experience has shown that it takes some time to get your eye in on the rocks and complexities of the Marginal Zone of the Carrock series; starting on the Mosedale series gabbros also means getting most of the climbing out of the way before examining the rocks. Vehicles may be parked in Mosedale or off the road just to the north of the hamlet. Alternatively, there is plenty of space to park off the road 1.5 kilometres to the north of Mosedale, beneath the crags of Scurth (NY 355335). The excursion ends close to here.

Figure 17 shows a simplified map of the eastern part of the Carrock Fell Complex with the localities shown. Figure 18 shows a schematic N-S vertical section through the eastern part of the complex and Figure 19 is a simplified map of the Further Gill Sike region showing localities 10-15.

The Mosedale series
Proceed up the hillside behind the farm at the north end of Mosedale. Examination of the rocks exposed on Black Crag just north of Mosedale is not particularly instructive at this stage.

Locality 1 (NY 355324). The contact between the folded Skiddaw Slates to the south and the Southern Marginal Gabbros (SMG) to the north rises near - vertically up the steep hillside to the left of the crags on the skyline. The contact is irregular on a scale of 5-20m and appears to be controlled by major joint planes in the slates. Outcrops of the actual contact can be located approximately 50m in height directly above the barn doors of the most northerly buildings in Mosedale. The gabbro is medium-grained and relatively homogeneous. The dark colour can be attributed to the abundant secondary amphibole. The primary mineralogy is plagioclase, clinopyroxene

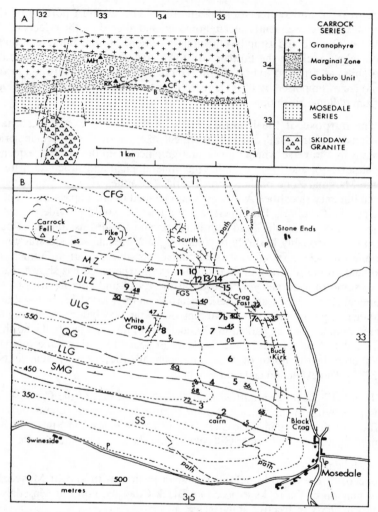

Figure 17. (A) Sketch map of the eastern part of the Carrock Fell Complex (modified after Eastwood *et al.*, 1968) showing the Mosedale and Carrock series. The positions of localities A-D are shown. (B) Enlarged sketch map of the southeastern part of the complex showing the units of the Mosedale series gabbros (SMG - Southern Marginal Gabbro: LLG - Lower Leucogabbro; QG - Quartz Gabbro; ULG - Upper Leucogabbro; ULZ - Upper Layered Zone) and the Marginal Zone (MZ) and Carrock Fell Granophyre (CFG) of the Carrock series. The localities are numbered 1-15. The dip of the layering/lamination in the Mosedale gabbros is also shown. FGS = Further Gill Sike; SS = Skiddaw Slates; s = sheepfolds; P = parking locations.

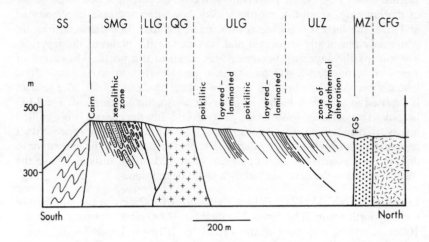

Figure 18. Sketch section through the Mosedale series (approximately along grid-line easting 352) showing the attitude of the layering/lamination and the main contacts.

and Fe-Ti oxides. Biotite is not uncommon in rocks close to the margin and in the vicinity of large xenoliths further from the margin. The gabbro is chilled against the Skiddaw Slates which are hornfelsed; locally in pelitic horizons, almandine garnet may be found.

Locality 2 (NY 352325). Follow the contact up the steep hillside until the zig-zag path from the west of Mosedale is intersected at a height of about 150m above the road. Follow this to a break in slope near a small wall and sheepfold, then take the path westwards for 150m to a small cairn. Here, weather permitting, there is an excellent panorama over the Mosedale series gabbros and the Carrock series granophyre forming the summit of Pike on the skyline to the north. Below this, and to the left, is White Crag and to the, right, the grass-covered upper reaches of Further Gill Sike and the top of Scurth crags. Steeply-dipping Skiddaw Slates crop out 20m west of the cairn which itself is on SMG.

Locality 3 (NY 351326). Proceed in a north-west direction for 160 m to some prominent outcrops of layered SMG. Modal layering occurs on scales up to 1m but is typically in the range 1-20 centimetres. The layering reflects differences in the modal proportions of primocryst plagioclase feldspar, clinopyroxene and Fe-Ti oxides (magnetite and ilmenite). Individual layers may be divided by differences in abundance of poikilitic clinopyroxene, defining an 'intercumulus layering'. The layering dips steeply (60°-80°) to the north-northeast.

Locality 4 (NY 351327). Traversing to the north, perpendicular to the strike of the layering, xenoliths, mostly of Skiddaw Slate, increase in abundance and size, the largest reaching several metres across. Smaller xenoliths are commonly plastically deformed and flattened in the plane of the layering. The dip of the layering becomes less steep to the north. This zone of xenolithic, banded SMG passes into a relatively massive, poikilitic leucogabbro poor in xenoliths, the Lower Leucogabbro (LLG). The contact is exposed in a 2 metre high crag behind a conspicuous sheepfold. The LLG becomes finer-grained towards the SMG over 2-3m; the contact is not chilled but is diffuse over a few centimetres. The LLG probably represents a replenishment event on this evidence. The contact appears to be vertical or to dip steeply towards the north and can be traced in the hillside above the sheepfold and to the east, marked by a slight depression.

Locality 5 (NY 352327). Follow the contact for 250m to the east before turning north again. The lower leucogabbro (LLG) here forms a zone 80-100m in width, widening to the east. It is diffusely banded with wispy, convoluted mafic laminae occurring locally. The layering dips to the north but at a shallower angle (50-60°) than in the Southern Marginal Gabbro (SMG). Small xenoliths, both of Skiddaw Slate and Eycott Volcanic material are present and increase in abundance towards the north.

Locality 6 (NY 352329). The LLG is in contact with a relatively homogeneous, finer grained, mesocratic quartz gabbro (QG). The contact is poorly exposed and appears to be gradational over 2-3m. Field relationships elsewhere indicate that QG post-dates the LLG. The QG here forms a zone 50m wide and passes northwards into a coarser, poikilitic leucogabbro, the upper leucogabbro (ULG), texturally similar but less mafic than LLG. The Quartz Gabbro is interpreted as having crystallised from a pulse of magma intruded into unconsolidated leucogabbro crystal mush. Apart from thin felsic veins which occur along joint planes throughout the gabbros, the QG is chemically the most evolved member of the Mosedale series. In addition to augite, it contains inverted pigeonite and also abundant quartz.

Locality 7 (NY 351330). A traverse through the Upper Leucogabbro, starting from outcrops 100m to the northwest of a prominent sheepfold, passes stratigraphically upwards (i.e., north) through two zones, each characterised by a coarse, massive, leucogabbro passing upwards into modally layered then laminated gabbro. Both layering and lamination dip to the north at 50-55°. The upper of these laminated zones is easily mapped along the length of the Mosedale series outcrop and corresponds to the 'fluxion gabbro' of earlier workers. It is more mafic than the lower laminated zone and pyroxenes (augite and hypersthene), oxides and plagioclase exhibit lamination. In the outcrops above Crag Fast (locality 7b), the lamination dips at c 40° to the north. In the crags above the scree slope (locality 7c) the upper layered-laminated zone is well exhibited. The banding occurs on a cm-m scale and dips at 35-30° to the north, shallower than elsewhere in the intrusion.

Localities 7b and c are worth visiting if time permits or if the weather higher up the fell is inclement. If the latter, an exit can be made down the path below Crag Fast (Strong Trod) and a traverse made across the Upper Layered Zone to the lower reaches of Further Gill Sike to examine units of the Marginal Zone of the Carrock series.

Locality 8 (NY 348330). Proceed up the fell to White Crags (c 350m) past another prominent but derelict sheepfold. A northerly traverse from the southern end of the crag passes from the QG through both poikilitic-banded-laminated zones of the ULG. Locally, a regular rhythmic, modal layering is developed; cm-scale layers of poikilitic clinopyroxene are regularly spaced at c 10 centimetre intervals. The upper laminated gabbro occurs at the northerly end of White Crag, where the dip of the lamination is 45-50° to the north.

Locality 9 (NY 346333). Further north, the outcrop is discontinuous but along the length of the Mosedale series is a zone of banded/laminated gabbros, locally rich in ilmenite and titanomagnetite, the Upper Layered Zone. Close to the upper reaches of Further Gill Sike, the banding is diffuse on a 10-20cm-scale and represents an increase in mafic/oxide minerals in an otherwise relatively homogeneous mesocratic gabbro. The gabbros along the northern margin have been variably affected by hydrothermal alteration, associated with the emplacement and cooling of the later Carrock series. The effect is to make the gabbros appear more melanocratic and locally mottled in hand-specimen, primarily due to development of retrograde actinolite and hornblende.

The Carrock series
An ascent of Carrock Fell can be made from here via Pike. Localities A to D, in the Carrock series, will be described later.

The itinerary continues with the examination of the rock types and field relations in the Marginal Zone of the Carrock series which crop out in a zone 50-100m wide, from Round Knott in the west to the lower reaches of Further Gill Sike in the east (Figure 19). The first locality is the line of small cliffs at the head of the scree slope on the northern margin of Further Gill Sike. The cliffs are best approached from above the obvious grassy gully at the top of the Sike. The scree slope below locality 10 is steep and unstable. **Rocks dislodged from this locality represent a hazard** for walkers ascending Carrock Fell and for others on the approach path which passes directly beneath at the foot of the scree slope.

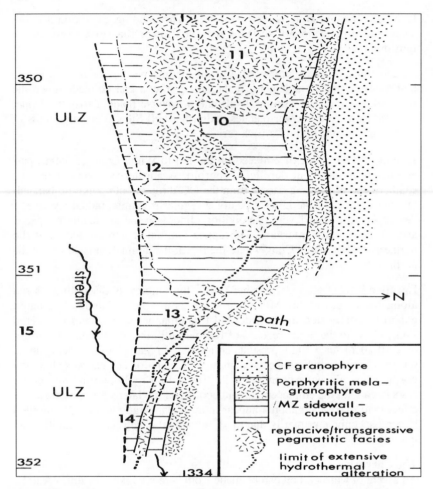

Figure 19. Simplified geological map of the Marginal Zone in the lower reaches of Further Gill Sike showing the positions of localities 10-15. Due to lack of continuous exposure, correlation of individual units is difficult; in part, the correlations are based on mineral- and bulk-chemical data. Within the zone of side-wall cumulates, there are internal contacts but in general the zone shows rapid systematic textural, modal and cryptic variations perpendicular to the southern contact against the ULZ gabbros. The primocryst mineralogy is plagioclase, clinopyroxene (augite - ferro-hedenbergite), magnetite, ilmenite, apatite and zircon. The rocks are orthocumulate in character, the proportion of trapped melt correlates with the percentage of interstitial granophyric intergrowth. The replacive and transgressive pegmatitic facies show an increase in grain-size and amount of quartz/alkali feldspar, their position corresponds approximately with the limit of extensive hydrothermal alteration.

Locality 10 (NY 350334). At this locality, a traverse can be made through the Marginal Zone. The rubbly outcrop extending from the north side of the grassy gully to the southern end of the line of cliffs is mainly granophyric ferrogabbro and pegmatitic granophyric ferrodiorite. These rock-types are better examined lower in Further Gill Sike. A traverse from south to north along the line of cliffs passes through the following units: 25m of mafic granophyre; 5m of hornfelsed granophyre (a stoped block of the CF granophyre); a 15m wide sub-vertical sheet of porphyritic melagranophyre. The latter has a vertical, chilled contact against grey, hydrothermally altered CF granophyre forming the northern end of the cliffs. Where the mafic granophyre is adjacent to the stoped block of granophyre is a narrow zone in which fine-grained melagranophyre with acicular pyroxene is veined by darker porphyritic melagranophyre.

Locality 11 (NY 349334). The rubbly slope above the line of cliffs is in heterogeneous, drusy, granophyric pegmatite. Locally, there is spectacular development of dendritic and platy pyroxene (ferroaugite, pseudomorphed by ferroedenite (amphibole) and ferroactinolite) forming individual growths up to 30 centimetres in size. These pegmatites are thought to have crystallised from water-saturated melts trapped beneath the roof of the intrusion.

Locality 12 (NY 350333). From the southern end of the cliffs, traverse into the gully and follow the steep path down Further Gill Syke. Just below the higher of the two prominent trees, in the north side of the gully, is one of the numerous, generally E-W trending dykes which cut both the Carrock and Mosedale series. These are broadly ferroandesite-dacite in composition and possibly represent chilled magmas similar to those from which the Carrock series crystallised.

Locality 13 (NY 351333). The path traverses northwards out of the gully and across the scree slope. Below the path, beneath a rowan tree, is a small buttress. Descend to the right (south) of the buttress into the gully. Outcrops between the stream and the base of the buttress are in granophyric ferrogabbro. The rocks are hydrothermally altered, but are conspicuous in their abundance of acicular apatite; individual prisms up to 1 centimetre in length are common. Locally, there is crescumulate development of pyroxene and plagioclase normal to the wall forming the southern margin of the Carrock series. The contact is not exposed but is approximated by the line of the stream. The ferrogabbros also contain abundant Fe-Ti oxides. Their abundant apatite serves to distinguish them from the oxide-rich gabbroic cumulates of the Mosedale series (locality 15) which occur on the southern side of the stream and extend towards the tree covered cliffs 200m to the south. Locally the ferrogabbros are coarser grained and grade into granophyric pegmatites which appear to be replacive. On the east face of the small buttress, such rocks have a sub-horizontal contact with finer-grained, grey melagranophyre similar to that seen at locality 10. Outcrops disappear northwards beneath bracken and scree.

Locality 14 (NY 351333). Descend 50m to where the stream crosses slabs which form the lowest outcrops within the Marginal Zone. Ten metres above the slabs the stream cuts through ferrogabbro, which grades rapidly to the north into ferrodiorite and granophyric ferrodiorite. In the slabs forming the stream bed, the latter is seen to be transgressive. The rock has a blotchy, pegmatitic appearance brought about by the heterogeneous and selective nature of the hydrothermal alteration. At the left side of the slabs (facing upstream) the granophyric ferrodiorite has a sharp, but unchilled contact with laminated ferrodiorite. On the right of the slabs, in the stream bank, there is a sharp, unchilled contact against mafic granophyre; 4m to the north, there is a rapid transition into porphyritic melagranophyre which then disappears beneath bracken and scree.

Locality 15 (NY 352333). Oxide-rich cumulate gabbros of the Upper Layered Zone of the Mosedale series can be seen in outcrops 50m to the south of the stream. These are hydrothermally altered with pervasive development of actinolite and hornblende. This alteration probably resulted from circulation of groundwater in a hydrothermal convective system associated with the emplacement and cooling of the later Carrock series. This hydrothermal circulation also altered the early-formed ferrogabbros and ferrodiorites of the Carrock Series itself and was probably responsible for the development of the replacive and transgressive pegmatites within the Marginal Zone.

Descend to the road and back to Mosedale.

Should you wish to ascend Carrock Fell from locality 9, localities A-D can be included to examine the western Marginal Zone and aspects of the Gabbro Unit of the Carrock series at Round Knott. Ascend to the summit via Pike. The plateau from Pike in the east to west of Carrock Fell summit is surrounded by a ramp composed of blocks of granophyre at first sight resembling a scree. This marks the boundary of an Iron Age earth-works and hill-fortification.

A) (NY 342336). The summit of Carrock Fell is of pink porphyritic granophyre. 300m south of the summit, there is a sharp contact against porphyritic melagranophyre representing the northern unit of the Marginal Zone.

B) (NY 340335) 250m to the south-west, a traverse can be made across the Marginal Zone. The contact with the gabbros of the northern margin of the Mosedale series is unexposed. Ferrogabbros of the Marginal Zone are realtered but can be seen to be rich in Fe-Ti oxides and apatite. The latter occurs as euhedral prisms forming up to 5 modal %. Traversing north, the ferrogabbro becomes visibly granophyric over 20-30m changing in composition to ferrodiorite, and develops a blotchy appearance due to selective hydrothermal alteration. The lamination is vertical and is produced by aligned tabular plagioclase crystals. There is a rapid transition to a zone of grey, porphyritic melagranophyre which extends some 35m to an unexposed contact with grey Carrock granophyre.

C) (NY 334336). Layered augite-plagioclase cumulates of the Gabbro Unit of the Carrock series (the diabase of earlier workers) crop out on Round Knott. The rocks are altered but layering is preserved. The contact with the Carrock Fell Gabbro or Marginal Zone is not exposed. Fine grained aplitic back-veining into hybrid intermediate rock, to the south of Round Knott, suggests that the Gabbro Unit was emplaced into the granophyre, locally re-melting it. Relationships along the inferred contact extending eastwards to Scruth support this conclusion but nowhere is the contact visible.

D) (NY 332339). Outcrops in the Gabbro Unit between Round Knott and Milton Hill are interesting for the occurrence of fine-grained and chilled blobs of basaltic andesite magma within the primary layering. The layering is locally disturbed and convoluted. These blobs presumably represent magma injected along layering within the consolidating crystal mush. Compositionally, they represent reasonable parental magmas for the Carrock series in general.

It is not worth a detour to examine the granophyre exposed on Rae Crags. Although locally hybridised, it is rather altered. The quickest way back to Further Gill Sike is via Carrock Fell and Pike.

ITINERARY 4

The Skiddaw Group of Hope Beck, Hopegill Head and Gasgale Gill

A. H. Cooper, British Geological Survey

1:25,000 map NY 12 or Outdoor Leisure Map 4

This excursion examines the stratigraphy and sedimentology of the Skiddaw Group north of the Causey Pike Thrust. It also looks at hornfelsed Skiddaw Group at the north edge of the Crummock Water Aureole.

The sequence is Arenig in age and of a turbidity current origin. The oldest beds are siltstones with subordinate greywackes (the Hope Beck Slates of Jackson, 1961 and 1978) (Figure 20, Localities 2 and 3). These are overlain by the Loweswater Formation, approximately 900m of greywacke sandstones (Localities 6-10, 21 and 22). Above these further siltstones (Kirkstile Slates of Jackson, 1978) contain abundant slump folds (Localities 11-21). The Loweswater Formation is well-defined, but the Hope Beck and

Kirkstile slates are best considered as informal terms until complete revision of the area is finished and their stratigraphical relationships fully understood. The Crummock Water Aureole is an elongate zone of hydrothermal alteration and bleaching some 30 kilometres long and up to 3 kilometres wide. It extends from near Egremont through Grasmoor to Causey Pike and is probably related to a fault-controlled granitic intrusion at depth (Fortey and Cooper, 1986; Cooper *et al.*, 1988). The northern edge of the aureole is gradational (Figure 20, Localities 20 and 21), whereas the southern edge is marked by the Causey Pike Thrust. This thrust marks the dividing line between the olistostrome of the Buttermere Formation and the less-disturbed Arenig sequence described above.

Two starting points are available for this circular trip: Hope Beck (NY 16922418), on a narrow, gated road only suitable for cars (parking for 6 cars), or Lanthwaite Green car park (NY 15882076) which is accessible by coach. If the starting point is Hope Beck follow localities 1-22; if the starting point is Lanthwaite Green follow localities 22, 2, 1, 3 and 21). The complete circular excursion involves 9 kilometres of walking and 650m of ascent. If two or more vehicles are available localities 21, 22, 2, 3 and 1 make a low-level half day trip involving 4 kilometres of walking and very little ascent.

Starting at Hope Beck (NY 16922418) head south along the footpath parallel to the wall. After 150m take the right fork that runs towards the smooth, pointed hill of Dodd, and after another 100m stop for the view.

Locality 1 (NY 16902392). Looking north-west the vista is along the Lorton valley to Lorton, Cockermouth and the Solway Firth (Iapetus suture?); in clear conditions the Scottish mountains with the Criffel 'granite', the highest part, can be seen. The Lorton valley is wide and broadly U-shaped with a few ice-smoothed roches moutonées such as Redhow Crag (1523) in the middle of the valley about 1 kilometre to the WSW. Much of the lower slopes of the valley are mantled with undulating till (boulder clay). North-west again, several low, wooded hills in the valley on the far side of Lorton (NY 15202700) are composed of morainic gravels. Dammed in to the south of these is an extensive, almost flat, fluvio-glacial terrace; this is clearly seen when driving through Lorton. In the lower part of Hope Beck the valley is barred by a small, slightly hummocky belt of moraine extending up onto the flank of Dodd and the lower part of Swinside. Hope Beck has cut a narrow V-shaped valley through this moraine into the rock below. Without the moraine the Hope Beck valley is a U-shaped, hanging valley, draining into the Vale of Lorton.

Locality 2 (NY 16862384). Continue south 100m to where Hope Beck and the wall intersect. Here, laminated and thickly laminated, grey siltstone and mudstone are exposed; there is also one thin and one medium bed of lithic greywacke sandstone. These beds are part of the Skiddaw Group below the Loweswater Formation (designated the Hope Beck Slates by Jackson, 1961;

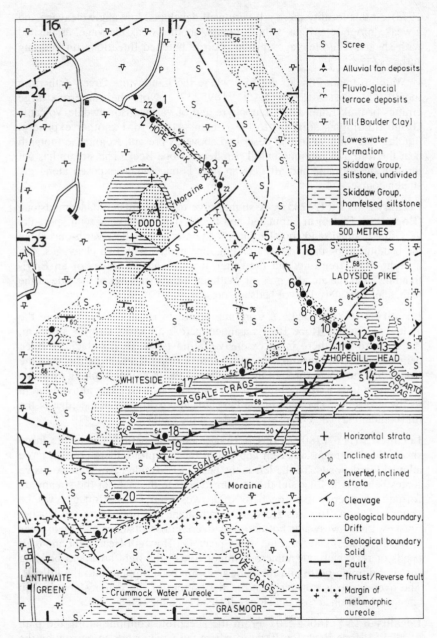

Figure 20. Geolosgal map of the area between Hope Beck and Gasgale Gill.

1978). At this locality there is a very well-developed low-angle cleavage and a weak, upright cleavage with, in places, another weak cleavage, associated with shears. The cleavages produce cross-hatched lineations on bedding surfaces.

Walk upstream 70m to the ford where the Lanthwaite Green path from locality 22 crosses the beck (NY 16952375). Note the numerous large erratics of pink Ennerdale Granophyre and of various Borrowdale Volcanic Group lithologies adjacent to the stream. At the ford another exposure, lithologically similar to that described above, is present. Rejoin the footpath near the ford and continue uphill parallel to Hope Beck. The stream has cut through the moraine and after 350m rock is once again exposed along the stream course.

Locality 3 (NY 17272353). A slight gorge exposes siltstone and mudstone (Hope Beck Slates) in laminated and thickly laminated beds with sporadic, very fine-grained sandstone laminae; load-casts and shallow wash-outs show the bedding to be uninverted. Bedding dips gently, with two cleavages, one upright, NW- trending and the other at a low-angle; traces of an ENE-trending cleavage are also present. With the loose exposures at the side of the path, approximately 13m of beds are present.

Locality 4 (NY 17402325). Continue upstream about 300m to where the valley widens and Hope Beck meanders across a narrow strip of alluvium. Adjacent to this there is an extensive, almost flat, fluvio-glacial terrace dammed in by the terminal moraine across Hope Beck; note the way the stream has cut down through the terrace and the moraine. Looking up Hope Beck and a little to the right, a tributary stream has formed an alluvial fan in its lower reaches. The apex of the fan starts approximately at the edge of the till (boulder clay) that blankets the sides of the valley.

Locality 5 (NY 17802293). Continue along the path 500m to the large sheepfold. Upstream, adjacent and left of the sheepfold, there are two more alluvial fan deposits. To the left is the peak of Ladyside Pike, with extensive screes below. The Pike and the un-named spur to the right of the stream are formed of steeply dipping beds of Loweswater Formation greywacke younging south. Towards Hopegill Head, along the line where the heather finishes, the Loweswater Formation is overlain by siltstones and mudstones (Kirkstile Slates) that form the rocky peak. On Hopegill Head light and dark bands of rock pick out numerous minor folds;' the light areas are bedding surfaces dipping north and the dark areas are beds dipping into the hillside. The overall dip is northerly and at the bottom of the major slabs the dip changes direction across the Hopegill Head syncline (Figure 20).

Locality 6 (NY 18002270). From the sheepfold continue along the path parallel to Hope Beck for 300m to where the valley starts to narrow by the first small scree (3m x 15m) on the west side. Here are the first exposures of the Loweswater Formation dipping steeply south-southeast. In the heather there are numerous small exposures of greywacke showing convolute and cross-laminated bedding (Bouma "C" units, Bouma, 1962); a few parallel-laminated ("B" units) are also present. Look for way-up evidence which shows that the sequence is younging upstream. Do not hammer these small exposures; good examples of sedimentary structures are easily available from the screes 100m upstream.

Locality 7 (NY 18052261). 100m upstream from locality 6, on the east side, there are exposures of vertically dipping Loweswater Formation. Thin, medium and thick beds are present including a few "A-B-C" Bouma sequences with graded beds ("A" units), parallel-laminated beds ("B" units) and cross-laminated beds ("C" units); a few siltstone (Bouma "D" units) and pelagic mudstone beds (Bouma "E" units) are also present. Some of the "A-B" units are micaceous and matrix-rich; some beds have lenticular patches with calcite cement that produce a brown, weathered crust. One high-angle cleavage with a normal bedding-cleavage relationship (for beds younging to the south) is present. Nearby a low-angled cross-cutting cleavage also occurs.

Locality 8 (NY, 18092256). Continue upstream for 80m to where the stream forks and the path bears left adjacent to a small waterfall. The thickest beds in the sequence crop out here with well-developed Bouma "A-B-C" units. Some of the water-worn surfaces show the sedimentary structures well; all the beds young southwards with a near-vertical dip.

Locality 9 (NY 18092256 to 182122480). Upstream for 200m from the waterfall the bedding thickness decreases to mainly thin, with a few medium, beds. "A" units become scarce, "B" units uncommon and the greywacke beds are dominantly cross-laminated and convolute-laminated "C" units. Some flute marks and groove casts occur on a few bedding planes; these structures show a southerly derived sediment source. Follow the stream uphill until the stream gully narrows; here the path continues a little above the stream on its east bank.

Locality 10 (NY 18262242). Near the sharp bend and fork in the headwaters of the stream numerous craggy exposures, just east of the stream, show a sequence with diminishing amounts of greywacke and increasing siltstone. Sedimentary structures indicate younging to the south, but there is also some minor folding and faulting. Two cleavages are present, one well-developed and upright, the other sporadic and low-angled. Just upstream from this locality the Loweswater Formation is faulted against the overlying siltstone and mudstone (Kirkstile Slates).

Locality 11 (NY 184222). Extensive screes are present below Hopegill Head. These have yielded graptolites including *Phyllograptus angustifolius* and others indicative of the *Isograptus gibberulus* Zone; the graptolites are fairly scarce. Follow the grassy stream course uphill, then take the grassy tract (ESE) to the rocky hump on the ridge. North of Hopegill Head, along the stream course, there are numerous exposures of siltstone (Kirkstile Slates) with sporadic, very thin, very fine-grained sandstone beds which indicate that the succession youngs southwards to the top of the stream. (An alternative route to Hopegill Head, avoiding the steep rocks below it, can be taken from locality 10. Bear right (SW), diagonally across the bottom of the screes, then up the grassy slope to the col (NY 18062217). Continue east along the ridge to Hopegill Head and Locality 14).

Locality 12 (NY 186223). At the rocky hump, just N of Hopegill Head, the lithology is laminated siltstone and mudstone with subordinate sandstone laminae (Kirkstile Slates). These beds have complicated, sheared folds (slump folds?), refolded by later, tectonic folds with an upright, axial-planar cleavage; there is also a low-angled fracture cleavage. Compare this exposure with Locality 13 to see the local variability in cleavage development.

Locality 13 (NY 18632229). 50m south of locality 12 there is a grassy area with a tumbled-down slate wall almost along the edge. Here the core of the Hopegill Head syncline is exposed. The north limb is upright and the south limb more gentle with well-developed minor folds exposed all the way up to the summit. The path traverses the northerly dipping bedding-plane slabs (long limbs of folds) and cuts up through the southerly dipping limbs (see also stop 5). Looking east from Locality 13 there is a fine view of Hobcarton Crag, the well-developed north-facing head of the straight, glacial U-shaped valley occupied by Hobcarton Gill.

Locality 14 (NY 18572216). At the summit of Hopegill Head there are fine views illustrating many aspects of the local geology. East is Grisedale Pike and to the west, Gasgale Crags; both have grey screes dominantly composed of siltstone fragments. By contrast, the view southwards, of the ridge next to Causey Pike, through Long Combe (with the oblique path running up it) to Scar Crag and Grasmoor shows screes with a brown and reddish tinge. These fells form part of the elongate, hydrothermally altered, and in places slightly hematised, Crummock Water Aureole. (Fortey and Cooper, 1986; Cooper *et al.*, 1988). This alteration has hornfelsed and hardened the rock allowing higher and steeper crags to form on these hills. Note the hanging cirque of Dove Crags on Grasmoor and the dissected, till-covered slopes below it. Dove Crag is delineated by well-developed N-S and E-W joint sets. West, along Gasgale Crags, the end of Crummock Water is visible. Just right of this, screes start abruptly along a straight line at the foot of the crags. This is the line of the Gasgale Thrust which throws complexly folded (slump and tectonic folds) beds of siltstone and subordinate greywacke sandstone (Kirkstile Slate Formation) over the younger, dominantly siltstone and mudstone succession below (also Kirkstile Slate Formation).

The rocks at Hopegill Head summit are dominantly siltstone (Kirkstile Slates), but with numerous convolute and cross-laminated greywacke sandstone beds which indicate that the sequence is the correct way up. 20m north from the summit there is an anticline parallel to the syncline described at stop 13. Walk west from the summit and follow the path along the ridge noting the numerous changes in dip direction as you cross the many minor folds exposed here. A fault is crossed and the proportion of sandstone increases, then the path drops down to a small grassy col, the junction with the alternative route from locality 11.

Locality 15 (NY 17192208). 100m west of the grassy col, where the path deviates to the N of the ridge, a well-developed upright cleavage and minor folds are visible.

Locality 16 (NY 17552211). Continue 550m west along the ridge path to the small, quarry-like exposure (one of the few places to shelter around here).

At this exposure siltstone with subordinate sandstone beds is folded into well-developed, gently plunging, minor folds with sporadic axial planar shears.

Locality 17 (NY 17072196). Head west along the ridge path to Whiteside noting the numerous folds with low-angle and upright cleavages. As Whiteside is approached well-exposed minor folds are exposed on the south side of the peak. These folds step down Gasgale Crags towards the Gasgale Thrust and have a low-angle cleavage with numerous shear planes. As you walk down the path at the end of Gasgale Crags note the numerous changes in dip associated with the minor folding.

Locality 18 (NY 16902162). On the steepest, rocky part of the path well-exposed minor folds with a fairly low-angled (44°) and, in some places, fanned , axial-planar cleavage occur. This sequence is dominantly siltstone (Kirkstile Slates) with about 5% greywacke sandstone with convolute and cross-laminated structures (Bouma "C" units) which indicate that the beds are the correct way up.

Locality 19 (NY 16902158). Where the rocky scramble finishes and the path starts to level out, the Gasgale Thrust cuts the ridge. East, along Gasgale Crags, the thrust can be clearly seen along the foot of the crags. As the thrust is crossed the lithology changes to dark grey siltstone and the topography becomes less craggy. The bedding in these complexly (slump) folded beds is difficult to see and the cleavage forms the dominant foliation.

Locality 20 Whin Ben (NY 16572124). The lithology here is dominantly siltstone with sporadic sandstone laminae. The path descends steeply from Whin Ben passing through an evenly dipping sequence of medium-dark grey laminated siltstones. Note the colour of these beds or take a loose sample to compare with those at Locality 21.

Locality 21 (NY 164120898). Near the foot of Whin Ben, just before the path becomes grassy and the gradient eases, the rock debris is hornfelsed siltstone (Kirkstile Slates), light to medium grey and weathered beige (compare with stop 20). These rocks form part of the gradational northern margin of the Crummock Water Aureole. Where this path becomes grassy bear left along a narrow path that curves for 80m to join the high Gasgale Gill path. Turn right, downhill, along this path then, after a few metres, there is a large rowan tree. The rock exposures from here to the stream are hornfelsed siltstone with subordinate, laminated to very thin-bedded greywacke. These rocks display well-developed slump folds, some are bedding confined, others have truncated tops suggesting erosion and/or shear of their upper parts. Brecciation, disruption and boudinage are also common, especially in the thin greywacke beds. BE CAREFUL, THIS HILLSIDE IS STEEP, SLIPPERY AND DANGEROUS. IT HAS LOOSE BLOCKS WHICH COULD BE DISLODGED ONTO THE BUSY FOOTPATH BELOW! Near the stream the proportion of greywacke beds increases rapidly as the gradational upper boundary of the Loweswater Formation is crossed.

Return to Lanthwaite Green car park via the footpath over the bridge, or walk back along the foot of Whiteside and Dodd to Hope Beck car park, 3 kilometres away.

Locality 22 (NY 160522367). Approximately 1.5 kilometres along the Hope Beck path there are rocky exposures of Loweswater Formation. These beds of greywacke sandstone with subordinate siltstone dip about 45°. They show well-developed Bouma turbidite units; mainly "B-C" and "C" units, but some "A-B-C" (see stops 6 and 7 for details). Truncated cross-lamination and the Bouma sequences show the beds to be the correct way up, younging southwards. The siltstone beds here are cut by a low-angle cleavage. Continue north along the paths to stops 2 and 1 and then to the Hope Beck car park.

ITINERARY 5

The Buttermere Formation (Skiddaw Group) in the Robinson Area

B. C. Webb, British Geological Survey

1:25,000 maps NY 11 and 12 or Outdoor Leisure Map 4

The geology of the Robinson area is complex. This excursion is most suitable for those with sufficient grasp of structural geology to pose their own questions and seek out the pertinent evidence. The best exposure is often on steep, craggy ground where caution and correct attire are essential. In wet and mist weather the steep ground can be very dangerous.

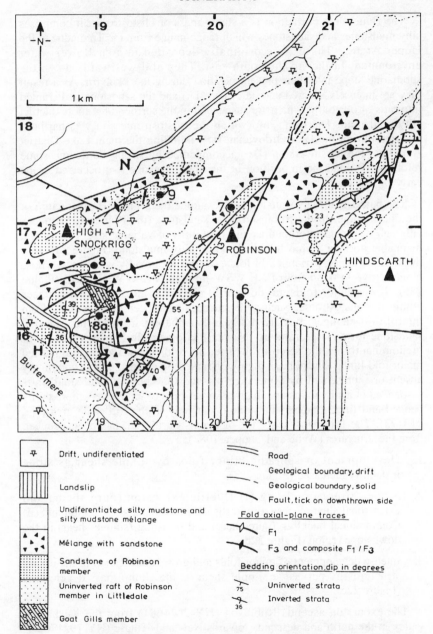

Figure 21. Geological sketch map of the Robinson area showing localities (numbered). H - Hassness, N - Newlands Hause.

The Buttermere Formation is a slump mass or olistostrome. It comprises silty mudstones and sandstones which range in age from the Tremadoc to the Upper Arenig. These were originally deposited in a shallower water environment farther to the south-east. They slid westwards down the submarine slope into their present position during the Llanvirn. As a result they are intensely sheared and deformed (D_1) and the sandstone is disrupted into rafts or olistoliths which are suspended in the surrounding, more ductile, silty mudstone. The basin into which the olistostrome slid was partially inverted during the later Ordovician (D_2) initiating the main Lake District Anticline. Further inversion (D_3), accompanied by strong flattening, some refolding (F_3) and the imposition of the main cleavage (S_3) occurred in the early Devonian.

The purpose of this excursion is to examine the primary (D_1) structure of the olistostrome. In the Robinson area, sandstone (the Robinson Member), although disrupted into boudins and olistoliths of variable size, occurs at a mappable horizon within the surrounding silty mudstone (Figure 21). It is disposed on major, periclinal, F_1 folds, overturned broadly westwards, whose hinges curve in trend from ENE-WSW through N-S to WNW-ESE (Figure 23a). These major folds are developed above D_1 thrust or slide surfaces within the olistostrome. Such slide surfaces have been demonstrated from microfloral changes, but are not readily apparent in the field. Massive sandstone forms large rafts up to over 1 kilometre in length which occur predominantly on the steep to inverted F_1 fold limbs. On the uninverted major fold limbs sandstone is highly disrupted by extension; it is commonly absent or represented by a mélange of sandstone boudins and small rafts suspended in a silty mudstone matrix. Larger rafts of uninverted, more thinly bedded and finer grained sandstone occur only in the Littledale area (NY 213173). The following sequence of events during D_1, has been deduced from the structures (Webb and Cooper, 1988).

1. Development of sporadic minor folds by simple shear as slope instability increased (Figure 22a).

2. Slope failure involving (i) Ductile extension (pure shear) and extensional slide planes (simple shear) in the upper slope region and (ii) Contractional buckling (pure shear) and thrusting (simple shear) in the downslope region (Figure 22b)

3. Intense development of minor folds and gross modification of the earlier structures by pervasive simple shear as the slump mass decelerated (Figure 22c).

The excursion ascends Robinson (NY 2011681) from the Keskadale valley in the north and descends towards Newlands Hause (NY 192176). If two vehicles are available it is possible to start from Chapel Bridge (NY 231193) and finish at Newlands Hause or in the Buttermere valley at either

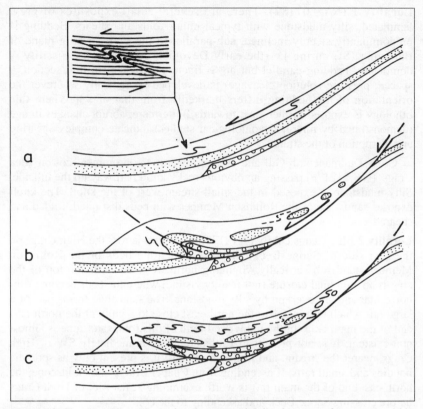

Figure 22. Sketch sections illustrating the sequential development of structures within a major slump (after Webb and Cooper, 1988). See text for details.

Hassness (NY 187158) or Buttermere Village (NY 176170). Parking space is available at all these localities but that at Hassness is limited. Variations of the route allow for the inclusion of Goldscope Mine (NY 2271851), Goat Crags and/or the west flank of High Snockrigg (NY 187169). The route described assumes only one vehicle is available in which case it should be parked in Keskadale at any of the roadside spaces between the start of open ground at NY 204185 and Newlands Hause. The circuit from here is some 10 kilometres long and involves some 500m of ascent. The geology and localities are given in Figure 21.

From the parking spot descend to and cross Keskadale Beck (the ground is very wet and the stream crossing can be problematical after heavy rain). Ascend gradually, eastwards, across the lower, drift covered slopes to enter the small valley of Dudmancomb Gill.

Locality 1 (NY 207182). There are several small exposures of grey, laminated, silty mudstone with typical minor folds and shears. Bedding is predominantly steeply inclined, sub-parallel to the ENE-striking plane of flattening (S_3) during D_3 (the early Devonian deformation). Fissility is dominantly bedding-parallel but an S_3 fracture cleavage (in thin section, a spaced, pressure solution cleavage) is developed sporadically wherever the orientation of the bedding differs markedly from that of S3. Where this lithology is exposed farther west towards Buttermere, abrupt changes in age (demonstrated by micropalaeontological studies) indicate complex shearing and disruption of the strata.

Cross Dudmancomb Gill and ascend towards the prominent col on Blea Crags (NY 212178) passing an obvious rocky knoll half way up the hillside. Silty mudstone is exposed in the small stream west of the knoll. The knoll exposes sandstone of the Robinson Member with beds disrupted, folded and sheared.

Locality 2 Blea Crags col (NY 212178). Look east across the High Crags on the east side of Scope Beck. Massive sandstone beds of the Robinson Member stand sub-vertically, younging north-west. Towards the top of the crag is an anticlinal closure (not readily visible) where the beds become sub-horizontal and are overlain by silty mudstone. The sandstone forms part of a large raft which terminates to the north-east close to a gully at the north-east end of the main crag. In the uninverted limb of this fold, sandstone is almost non-existent. It is not present in Littledale Crag, immediately SW of High Crags, nearer the stream, and farther north-east it is present only as sporadic boudins and small rafts. If ascending from Chapel Bridge and Goldscope, the north-east end of the main raft is worth examining at the foot of High Crags before crossing Scope Beck and ascending to the col.

From the col continue south-southwest up the ridge for some 150m, crossingly the first rocky prominence to a second, small col.

Locality 3 (NY 212177). The slabs overlooking the reservoir expose excellent F_1 minor folds of the Robinson Member on the uninverted limb of a major F_1 fold. A second set of open folds plunge down the slabs refolding the F_1 folds. The main cleavage (S_3) is almost axial-planar to the F_1 folds where these trend north-east, but superimposed over them where they trend more northerly. This is best seen some 20m above the base of the slabs towards their north end. Stereographic analysis of data from these folds relates the cleavage to the later, open folds (Figure 23b). Dispersion of the F_1 axes (Figure 23b) indicates low-angle extension but also implies a component of extension with a steeper inclination. The low-angle extension is in a plane parallel to the mean orientation of the univerted fold limbs. The generation of the F_1 folds is related to bedding plane slip during slumping (Webb and Cooper, 1988) and so this dispersion of the axes is considered primary. The steeper component of extension may be a result of the F_3 refolding.

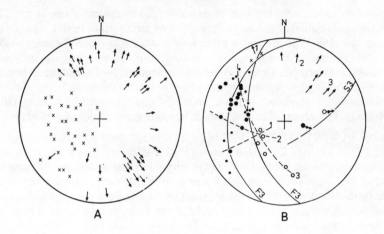

Figure 23. Equal-area projections of data from the Robinson Member.

a) F_1 axes (arrows) and axial-plane poles (crosses) for the whole of the Robinson area.

   F_3 refolding about S_3 (which is steeply inclined and strikes between E and ENE) has dispersed the poles to F_1 axial-planes to both N and S. It has also increased the plunge of F_1 axes towards these quadrants. Prior to D_3 the F_1 axial-planes were curved with an easterly dip increasing from gentle to steep. The well-dispersed F_1 axes would have lain on a single plane, sub-parallel to the gentle, uninverted fold limbs. The easterly dip of this slide plane is in opposition to the direction of slumping because the Robinson area lies on the SE dipping limb of the D_2/D_3 Lake District Anticline.

b) D_1/D_3 interference structures, Blea Crags. This shows: poles to bedding in the uninverted F_1 fold limbs (open circles), the inverted F_1 fold limbs (filled circles), undifferentiated (dots), great circles (dashed lines) and axes (arrows) for the F_1 folds, great circles (labelled F_3) and axes (double headed arrows) for F_3 folding of the F_1 limbs, poles to S_3 (crosses), and the mean S_3 great circle (labelled S_3). For explanation see text.

At this locality the Robinson Member comprises thin-bedded fine-grained greywacke sandstone interbedded with silty mudstone and is predominantly uninverted. Along High Snab Bank, the adjacent silty mudstones have yielded lower Arenig microfossils.

Scramble up the last two steep steps in the ridge. The lithology becomes more silty and the bedding more disturbed. The S_3 cleavage is locally well developed and associated with minor F_3 folds. At the top of the steep section of the ridge leave the path, which continues up the north-east ridge of Robinson, and contour south into Littledale. Sandstone soon reappears and becomes increasingly massive. Beds stand sub-vertical and young north. This is the continuation of the steep, major F_1 fold limb seen in High Crags. To the east sandstone is absent on the gentler, uninverted fold limb. The craggy slope of Hindscarth on the east side of Littledale exposes the overlying grey silty mudstone which has yielded upper Arenig graptolites. This suggests that the Robinson Member is equivalent, in age, to the Loweswater Formation (see itinerary 4). Follow the sandstone beds west and then south-west along strike to the first of three broken crags which lie along the west side of Littledale.

Locality 4 (NY 211173). Thick beds of coarse-grained greywacke sandstone and fine-grained conglomerate are well-exposed and exhibit bottom structures and graded bedding. Local silty mudstone injections penetrate the sandstone beds along joint-like fractures. Towards the south-west end of the crag the sandstone becomes increasingly massive with common quartz veining. Contacts are not exposed but the massive sandstone terminates abruptly against more gently, easterly dipping, thinly-bedded sandstone and siltstone which in uninverted. This raft of uninverted Robinson Member becomes gradually more disrupted to the north and passes into a sandstone mélange. To the south its termination is more abrupt. It is exposed in the second of the broken crags, some 250m north of Brunt Crags (NY 207167).

Locality 5 (NY 207169). This crag exposes slabs of greywacke sandstone and silty mudstone with open F_3 folds comparable with those at Blea Crags. On the north side of the crag the beds are uninverted but to the south they become inverted (a discrete fold hinge cannot be identified) and are sheared and truncated against pale, greenish-brown, silty mudstone. In the Grasmoor area, some 3km to the north (see itinerary 4) similar bleaching of silty mudstone is related to metasomatism by fluids emanating from a buried granitic intrusion (Cooper, *et al.*, 1988). Although bleached rocks crop out over much of the summit area of Robinson, quartz-tourmaline veining, common in the Grasmoor area, is rare. Contour south, above Brunt Crags, to reach the main ridge path and fence overlooking Gatesgarthdale. Ascend the path for a short distance and cross the fence to Hackney Holes.

Locality 6 Hackney Holes (NY 202162). The impressive fissures are part of the back-scar to a large, interglacial, landslip (Figure 21) which extends ESE to past Littledale Edge (NY 210160). The instability is due to an E-W trending fault which crosses this ground. The fault plane dips moderately to the south i.e. towards the valley. Instability was increased by glacial oversteepening of the valleyside.

Follow the path over bleached, silty mudstone to the summit of Robinson and continue north to above Robinson Crags.

Locality 7 Robinson Crags (NY 202172). A recumbent, major F_1 anticline, facing north-west is present in the crag. Sandstone in the core of this structure crops out along the top of the crag. Beds are locally uninverted, but descent onto the crag immediately west of Red Gill (the head of Dudmancomb Gill) shows that the uninverted limb is largely sheared out. If conditions permit, the main closure can be viewed by descending a little towards the south-west end of the crag and looking back toward the north-east.

The sandstone outcrop in the core of the Robinson F_1 anticline can be traced south-west along the west flank of Robinson towards the top of Goat Gills. Minor F_1 folds are present but the beds are commonly steeply inclined or inverted. The major, uninverted limb is poorly represented. Cross Buttermere Moss, skirting the top of Goat Gill to drier, more elevated ground above Goat Crags.

Locality 8 Goat Crags (NY 188165). A major F_1 anticline plunges south-east through Goat Crags. A debris flow with siltstone and fine-grained sandstone clasts (the Goat Gills Member) crops out in the core of this structure. Medium to fine-grained sandstone and siltstone of the Robinson Member are well-preserved on the inverted major fold limb where F_1 and F_3 minor folds are well-displayed. The uninverted limb mainly consists of silty mudstone and sandstone mélange but a number of small rafts of uninverted, medium to coarse-grained sandstone occur in the hinge region, at the top of the crag. Relatively undisturbed silty mudstone overlies the mélange and crops out above Goat Gills and at the north-west end of Goat Crags.

Sporadic exposures of silty mudstone mélange occur on the highest ground above Goat Crags. Southwestwards this passes into sandstone mélange just above the crag. Immediately above a prominent gully at the highest point of the crag a raft of fairly massive coarse-grained sandstone is clearly truncated against silty mudstone to the west. The truncation surface is coated with a breccia of sandstone fragments. Similar breccia occurs both in the crags below and at Littledale (in the vicinity of Locality 4.). It is thought to be of primary (D_1) generation. A larger, uninverted sandstone raft crops out along the top of the crag a little further south-east, but access is difficult.

It is possible to descend to Hassness from the north-west end of Goat Crags or even down some of the gullies. This involves very steep ground and some scrambling on very loose rock. It is inadvisable for a large party but a small, competent group should manage.

Locality 8a Goat Gill (NY 190161). This may be visited if descending from Goat Crags (Locality 8) or by ascending the path from Hassness.

The spur between Goat Gill and Hassnesshow Beck, above the small reservoir (which is a drinking water supply), exposes medium to fine-grained sandstone, inverted by F_1 and refolded over a medium-scale F_3 fold. A sheared contact with the stratigraphically underlying debris flow (the Goat Gill Member) is well-exposed at the foot of the steep cliff some 70m up the spur. The ground here is steep and very slippery when wet. A fall from here into Goat Gill would be serious.

82 B. C. WEBB

From the top of Goat Crags, Moss Force can be reached directly across Buttermere Moss but the going is drier by first heading north to High Snockrigg and then skirting the moss along its western edge. If descending to Buttermere Village, the sandstone raft which outcrops on High Snockrigg can be examined. D_1 and D_3 structures are well-exposed on the south-east ridge leading down to Low Snockrigg (NY 183166).

Locality 9 Moss Force Crags (NY 195173). A sandstone raft crops out to the east of Moss Force. It forms the higher, slightly drier ground bordering Buttermere Moss on its northern side. Gently dipping, uninverted sandstone beds crop out above the crags and turn down steeply, northwestwards, in the cliff face. The monoclinal structure is probably of composite D_1/D_3 age. At its eastern end the raft terminates abruptly (NY 196173). To the west it passes into sandstone mélange which is also folded over the monocline.

The easiest descent to Newlands Hause is by the path down the spur west of Moss Beck. This descends over silty mudstone mélange which has yielded Tremadoc microfossils. From the hause a path leads back to the foot of Moss Force. In the upper waterfall a large sandstone boudin stands out impressively from the surrounding mélange of silty mudstone.

A return to the starting point is best made along the road (the valley bottom is very wet). Note the large protalus rampart below Moss Force Crags which is breached by High Hole Beck (NY 197176).

ITINERARY 6

The Skiddaw Group of Stoneycroft Gill, Causey Pike and Outerside

A. H. Cooper, British Geological Survey

Outdoor Leisure Map 4 or 1:25,000 map NY22

This excursion is a fairly strenuous full day trip involving 6km of walking and approximately 500m of ascent. If the weather is poor or only half a day is available then stops 1-8, returning along the mine track, make an easy, half day excursion involving 2km of walking and 150m of ascent. The trip has several aims: to show the olistostromic Buttermere Formation (and Robinson Member) of the Skiddaw Group, the normal siltstone facies of the Skiddaw Group (Kirkstile Slates) and its alteration by hornfelsing, and thrusting of the hornfelsed strata over unaltered rock. Turbidite sequences with good way-up evidence and both inverted and right way-up strata are visited. The geology and localities are given in Figure 24. General information on the Buttermere Formation can be found in the introduction to itinerary 5.

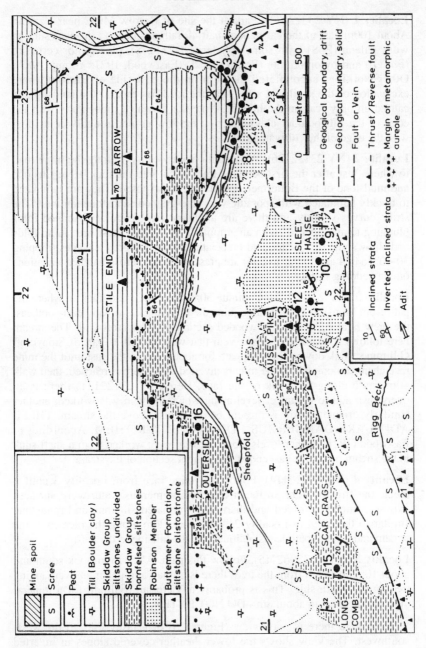

Figure 24. Geological map of the area around Causey Pike.

Locality 1 (NY 23322173). Park at the site of Barrow Mine, near Uzzicar. About 100m east of the car-park a shaft 40 fathoms deep (73m) was sunk to work galena (PbS) with some sphalerite ((ZnFe)S), plus minor cerussite (PbCO$_3$) and pyromorphite (Pb$_5$(PO$_4$).3Cl) (Eastwood, 1921; Young, 1987). Other workings encountered the vein on the east side of Barrow where excavation of the spoil and scree near the road has produced a landslip and caused an ugly scar on the hillside. Note the glaciated topography with the edge of the till (boulder clay) covering the low ground roughly coinciding with the edge of the cultivated fields.

Locality 2 (NY 23132126). Walk south from locality 1 along the mine road to where, just after the first bend the track is cut into the rock. Here siltstone and mudstone of the Buttermere Formation are exposed. They are laminated to thickly laminated with sporadic very fine-grained sandstone laminae. The strike curves slightly and there are abundant tight angular Z-shaped folds plunging to around 120° with an amplitude of 0.3-1m; these are slump folds and show some dislocation and brecciation. Two fracture cleavages (dipping 30-40° to 024 and c. 52° to 234) are present forming cross-hatched lineations on the bedding surfaces.

Locality 3 (NY 23102122). Continue 50m along the mine track to where the path from Stonycroft Gill Bridge joins the mine track. Looking east-southeast the view is along a straight, wooded section of Stonycroft Gill. The stream here follows a quartz and galena vein that was worked as part of Stonycroft Gill mine. Walk downhill on the path for about 60m to the east until the mine race channel along which the miners diverted the stream is reached, then walk 40m south along the bank of the race. Here (NY 23122121) there is an overgrown adit to the upper level along which the vein was worked; another similarly orientated adit is present below it just above the stream. THESE ADITS ARE DANGEROUS - DO NOT ENTER THEM. According to Eastwood (1921) further levels along the vein were worked from a shaft sunk in the stream bed at the east end of the straight section of the steam.

Locality 4 (NY 23112114). Follow the mine race from Locality 3 until it meets the stream. Here, in the stream bed, numerous water-worn surfaces expose complexly folded and disrupted laminated siltstone and mudstone similar to that seen at Locality 2. Walk back 20m along the race from the stream and a small path leads obliquely up the hillside to the west.

Locality 5 (NY 5. 22962115). Follow this path. After 150m look south and about 10m upstream from the trees there is a small adit under an overhanging tree on the south side. This is probably a Victorian trial adit for a mineral vein; it only goes in about 8m - DO NOT ENTER.

From here there is good view (Figure 25) of Causey Pike to the west-southwest. The view shows the lower, heather-covered slopes in inverted quartz-rich greywacke beds of Robinson Member (Sandstone rafts within the

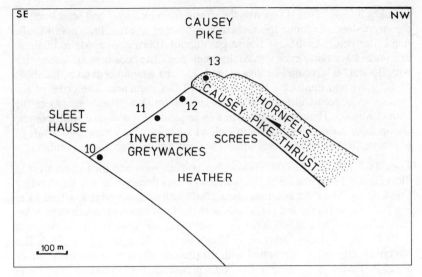

Figure 25. Causey Pike viewed from the east.

Buttermere Formation olistostome). This is capped by the crags of Causey Pike comprising hornfelsed siltstone and mudstone (Kirkstile Slates) within the Crummock Water aureole thrust southwards over the top of the olistostome (Cooper *et al.*, 1988). The thrust extends from beneath the east end of the Crummock Water Aureole and passes just north of Locality 6. It separates the highly contorted and slumped siltstone and mudstone of the Buttermere Formation, with folded and disrupted rafts of sandstone (Robinson Member), from less disrupted Skiddaw Group to the north.

Locality 6 (NY 22832120). Continue west along the path, then skirt south of the covered reservoir. This reservoir is on the site of the old smelting works for ore from Stonycroft mine. There is abundant slag, but also a pile of unused ore from the cobalt mine in Long Comb (NY 20582060) for which the Stonycroft Gill track was built. Follow the path from the reservoir west to where it crosses Stonycroft Gill.

Locality 7 (NY 22772120). Here there is a quarry exposing siltstone with up to 40% of fine-grained greywacke sandstone with parallel lamination (Bouma "B" unit) and cross-lamination (Bouma "C" unit). One coarse-grained medium-thick bed is present in the east of the quarry where many of the beds are lenticular and disrupted. This sequence strikes directly into convolute-folded, slumped siltstone and mudstone of the north and a dominantly greywacke sequence to the south. It marks the edge of a greywacke raft in the olistostrome Buttermere Formation.

Locality 8 (NY 22702115). Cross the stream from locality 7 and head south up the steep slope. Examine the numerous exposures as you climb uphill to the main Stonycroft Gill/Sleet Hause path about 100m above. Many of these exposures have fairly even dips to the south-east. The beds here are quartz-rich with Bouma "B" (parallel-laminated) and "C" (cross-laminated) units. Interbeds of siltstone and mudstone form 30-40% of the sequence. The order of the Bouma sequences and truncated cross-lamination show these beds to be the correct way up. These outcrops form a large patch of greywacke with sporadic slump folds surrounded by slump-folded siltstone. They represent a raft of sandstone (Robinson Member) within the olistostromic Buttermere Formation.

Locality 9 (NY 22252067). Follow the footpath west and then south-west to Sleet Hause. Here, at a cairn, the footpath crosses perpendicularly the Rowling End-Causey Pike Path; continue about 50m south over the ridge to where there is a good view. On the left is Catbells with the spoil heaps of Yewthwaite Mine from which galena and sphalerite were worked (Eastwood, 1921). To the south is the U-shaped glacial valley of Newlands Beck running up to Dale Head. The bottom of this valley is mantled with till (boulder clay) with extensive screes along its flanks. A hanging valley joins Newlands Beck between Dale Head and High Spy. A little to the right are Hindscarth and Robinson, also with a hanging valley between them where Scope Beck tumbles over Littledale Edge. On the valley side below the viewpoint and to the right is a small wood of native oak trees, relics of the natural vegetation of these hills.

Locality 10 (NY 22142070). Return to the Sleet Hause cairn and then head west 70m up the Causey Pike footpath to the first rock exposure. Here, and a little way round to the south of the ridge, quartz-rich greywacke is exposed. These thin, medium and thick beds show classic Bouma "B: and "C": units which, along with truncated cross-lamination and convolute lamination, prove the sequence to be inverted. About 50 km further along the path the rocks become disrupted, with tight, angular, slump folds with some quartz veining.

Most greywacke beds on this south side of Causey Pike, from here to 400m westwards, are inverted. They are complexly folded, sheared (Figure 26) and do not map out with any coherent relationship to the surrounding rocks which are dominantly brecciated, slump-folded and disrupted siltstones and mudstones with sporadic sandstone boudins. The greywackes here and at Locality 11 are sandstone rafts within the Buttermere Formation olistostrome.

Locality 11 (NY 21962074). About half-way between Sleet Hause and Causey Pike there are two grassy benches with cairns to the north of the path. At the upper of these cairns contour carefully round the south side of the hill 70m to a large outcrop of greywacke. There is a tight inverted anticline (Figure 26) that bears little relationship to the exposures to the west from which it is separated by a fault. If time permits, good sedimentary structures, including bottom structures, are exposed on the adjacent outcrops about 100m further west (NY 21872073).

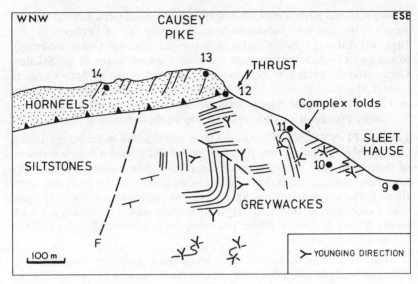

Figure 26. Causey Pike viewed from the south.

Locality 12 (NY 21922084). Return to the Causey Pike path and walk up to the prominent rocky cap at the Pike. The sequence becomes more silty and the folding more complex as the Causey Pike Thrust is approached; these are slump folds complicated by shear associated with the thrusting. Where the path meets the rocky top of Causey Pike the thrust is exposed and there are changes in hardness, colour and lithology of the rocks. The thrust plane dips at approximately 40°N. The overthrust strata are composed of bleached and hornfelsed Skiddaw Group siltstone and mudstone (Kirkstile Slates) with minor, sub-vertical, E-W trending tourmaline veins. These beds overlie dark grey siltstone with a lenticular breccia up to 30cm thick along the contact. The overthrust hornfels is part of the Crummock Water Aureole, and elongate zone of bleaching and tourmaline mineralisation probably associated with a buried granitic intrusion (Fortey & Cooper, 1986; Cooper *et al.*, 1988). The onward path involves a scramble up the rocks for about 20m. Two routes are used, one straight on, the other one to the right (north) and then up a gully. An alternative path to the left (south then west) contours the hill, drops slightly and them climbs up by-passing the steep rocks. This adds an extra 300m walking to reach the summit, but is useful in very wet or windy weather when rocks are slippery.

Locality 13 (NY 21882086). At the summit of Causey Pike the rock is light grey, (brown-weathered) horfelsed siltstone (Kirkstile Slates) with slump folds and narrow, cross-cutting, dark grey tourmaline veins. The view from Causey Pike looks east over Derwent Water and north to Bassenthwaite Lake. The lakes occupy a U-shaped glacial valley and are separated by a flat terrace of fluvioglacial and alluvial outwash mainly from the River Greta flowing through Keswick, but also from Newlands Beck. On the far side of Derwentwater the large, wooded crag (Walla Crag) is of Borrowdale Volcanic Group, the craggy topography of which contrasts with the mainly smooth slopes of the Skiddaw Group around Skiddaw to the north-northeast. Where the Skiddaw Group is hornfelsed in the Crummock Water Aureole it has the craggy topography evident on Causey Pike and the ridge running westwards. From the summit the line of the Causey Pike thrust is clearly visbile following the foot of these crags.

Locality 14 (NY 21802089). On the third minor hump in the ridge - taking Causey Pike as the first - the path cuts across and around a superb exposure of tourmaline veins cutting slump folds. (Please do not hammer and collect from here; there is much debris in the fallen blocks on the south and north flanks). The tourmaline veins have hard, tourmalinised wall-rock selvages, with a more readily weathered, crystalline tourmaline core, commonly with quartz (Fortey & Cooper, 1986). The slump folds here and along the ridge to the west are disharmonic.

Walk west about 400m where the level, peaty path starts to climb; bear right and head obliquely downhill towards the north-west to intersect the old mine road several hundreds of metres west of the prominent sheepfold, (21142120). Take the mine track west to Locality 15 or east to Locality 16. Alternatively, keen walkers may wish to continue west-southwest 1km over Scar Crags to a col (NY 20472050) then head north-east down Long Comb to join the track at the east side of Long Comb.

Locality 15 (NY 20582059). This optional stop is a visit to the workings of Scar Crag cobalt mine. This is reached by the steep grassy ledge which runs obliquely southwards up Long Comb from where the mine track and Long Comb path meet (NY 20622086). BE CAREFUL NOT TO DISLODGE ANY ROCKS ONTO THE BUSY PATH BELOW! At the top of the grassy rake, which follows the vein for 150m, there is an adit with another above it on the hillside (these adits are dangerous, do not enter them). Around these adits the NNE-SSW trending vein, along a minor fault, is exposed as several parallel bands of mineralisation up to 0.5m wide within an overall width of up to 1.5m. The vein is chlorite-rich quartz with arsenopyrite (FeAsS) weathering to pale green scorodite ($Fe^{+3}AsO_4.2H_2O$); prisms of white to buff apatite are also locally common in the spoil (B. Young pers. comm.). Red hematite staining is abundant in the wall-rock adjacent to the vein. Ixer *et al.*, (1979) record the following cobaltiferous minerals from the vein: alloclasite ((Co,Fe)AsS), glaucodot ((Co,Fe)AsS) and skutterudite ($CoAs_{2-3}$). Further details of the mineralisation are given by Young (in press). Return down the path and track to the sheepfold.

Locality 16 (NY 21322140). From the sheepfold head in a north-easterly direction contouring Outerside for about 300m until exposures are reached. Note the scree as you walk over it. It is hornfelsed siltstone and mudstone

(Kirkstile Slates), but not as massive as that seen on Causey Pike because here, on the northern side, the aureole has a gradational contact. Tourmaline veins are sparse in this marginal zone. Around this locality there are numerous well-exposed slump folds and a few exposures of intraformational breccia mainly of siltstone fragments in a mudstone matrix.

Locality 17 (NY 21442169). Progressing north-northeast along the east face of Outerside the degree of hornfelsing diminishes towards the gradational contact of the aureole so that at the Stile End-Outerside path the rock is almost unaltered siltstone and mudstone (Kirkstile Slates). Numerous minor slump-folds are exposed around here, but most of the beds dip to the east-northeast. Graptolites from this part of the sequence suggest the base of the *Didymograptus bifidus* Zone, some of the youngest strata recorded from west of Keswick. Other graptolites from the north face of Outerside suggest the *D. hirundo* Zone and indicate that the Arenig-Llanvirn boundary is present at this locality.

Head 200m south-east and return along the mine track to the Uzzicar car park.

ITINERARY 7

Devoke Water and Yoadcastle

D. Millward and B. Young, British Geological Survey

Outdoor Leisure Map 6 or 1:25,000 map SD19
This half to whole day excursion examines the Eskdale Granite and its contact relationships with the Skiddaw and Borrowdale Volcanic Groups (BVG); the volcanic sequence in the lower part of the lava pile is also studied. A characteristic volcanic feature of the granite contact in this area is the presence of greisens which have recently been shown to be common in the Eskdale Granite close to the margin (Young *et al.*, 1988). This alteration is interpreted as high temperature metasomatism along early-formed joints during the final cooling of the intrusion. The trip is mostly over rough fellside, with a total distance of 7km and a climb of only 240m. The geology and localities are given in Figure 27.

Cars may be left at the cross-roads (SD 17089770) on the fell road linking Eskdale Green with Ulpha. Proceed along the rough track, noting that it follows the approximate contact between the Eskdale Granite, seen in small exposures to the right and the Borrowdale Volcanic Group to the left. The very low grade of contact metamorphism in outcrops of the latter compared with elsewhere along the boundary suggests this is a faulted contact. At the head of the lake follow dry ground on the north side of the foot of Water Crag.

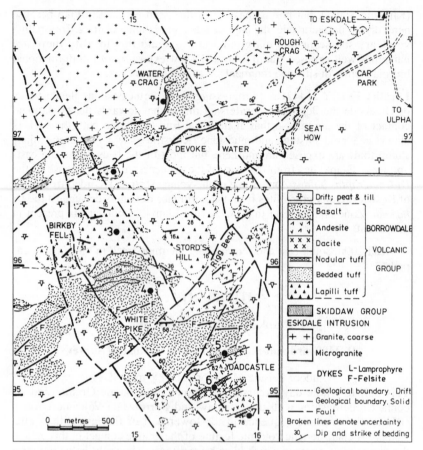

Figure 27. Geological map of the Eskdale granite and Borrowdale Volcanic outcrops around Devoke Water.

Locality 1 Water Crag (SD 153973). At the foot of Water Crag pale, fawn, Skiddaw Group silty mudstone forms low crags easily recognised by their slabby weathering along cleavage.

Proceed uphill to the pale grey, ice-smoothed exposures. The first of these is composed of coarse-grained pink granite, locally altered to quartz-topaz greisen. A few metres further up the hill much of the granite is conspicuously altered to quartz-topaz and quartz-mica greisen in bands up to 2m wide. In hand specimen topaz is identified as white to pale cream, anhedral crystals up to 8mm across in which the characteristic basal cleavage is readily seen. A little white mica is commonly present and, rarely, purple fluorite forms coatings on joints. At the extreme east of the exposures, nearest to the contact, a few rounded aggregates of pink andalusite up to 3cm across may be seen. Quartz-mica greisens are typically white, sparkling, mica-rich rocks here commonly form selvages to the quartz-topaz greisens.

Follow the eastern edge of the granite and greisen outcrops to the top of the hill where coarse-grained, pink granite forms ice-smoothed surfaces. Eastwards, towards the granite contact, quartz-topaz greisen is again present. At the extreme eastern end of the granite outcrop a rib up to 1m wide of quartz-andalusite rock parallels the contact with the Skiddaw Group for about 4m, though the actual contact is not exposed. This unusual rock is composed of abundant crystals of andalusite up to 8mm across in white to pale grey quartz with some flakes of white mica. A few lenses of almost pure white to pink andalusite up to 0.2m wide and 0.5m long are present within this rock. Please do not hammer this unique exposure. The origin of this rock is not clear though assimilation of aluminous sedimentary wallrock is likely.

A few metres further east of the Skiddaw Group outcrop hornfelsed andesite of the Borrowdale Volcanic Group is exposed. The brownish hue to these rocks is due to abundant microscopic biotite.

Locality 2 (SD 149968). Proceed to the low knoll south-west of cairns by the footpath from Devoke Water to Broad Oak. A small inlier of porphyritic microgranite within the Borrowdale Volcanic Group is exposed in ice-smoothed outcrops on the crest of the knoll. The microgranite contains abundant quartz and feldspar phenocrysts. Patchy alteration to quartz-mica greisen is conspicuous. Note the presence of residual quartz phenocrysts within the quartz-mica greisens. Fine-grained quartz-greisen occurs locally as ribs up to 10cm wide within the quartz-mica greisen.

On the north side of the knoll the greisen is cut by several ENE-trending, sub-vertical bands of coarsely crystalline, micaceous, specular hematite up to 20cm wide. Isolated plates of specular hematite also occur scattered throughout the greisen adjacent to the main segregation of this mineral.

Locality 3 Birkby Fell (SD 148963). Ascend the rough slopes of Birkby Fell. The lower part of the BVG in this area consists of weakly-bedded, coarse-grained basaltic lapilli tuff, generally dipping south. Although over short distances bedding is parallel, it can be appreciated that there are packages of tuff dipping in varying directions (for example at SD 14689636), and that some beds, when traced for tens of metres, thin out. Thin beds of accretionary lapilli and of abundant small clasts of siltstone and silty mudstone derived from the underlying Skiddaw Group can be identified locally. The essential, volcanic lapilli are generally angular, non-vesicular and heterolithic. These are primary eruptive products, possibly produced by the interaction of water with hot magma. This deposit, some 600m thick, represents the remnants of a tuff cone. There is little evidence in the lower part of this sequence, of erosion and channelling.

Locality 4 White Pike (SD 152958). Uphill the sequence becomes dominated by thin basaltic lava flows separated by thin, well-bedded tuff showing much evidence of reworking; for example, channeling, scour and fill structures and cross-lamination. The basaltic flows are dark green and grey and commonly highly pyroxene and plagioclase-phyric. They vary from about 12-50m thick and are simple flows with massive to highly amygdaloidal central parts and clinkery flow-breccias typical of aa-flows.

Locality 5 Yoadcastle (SD 157953). The termination of the episode of basaltic eruptions is marked by approximately 40m of bedded tuff exposed at the base of the northern side of Yoadcastle. These are parallel, medium-bedded to laminated, medium to coarse-grained, and locally cross-laminated. The clastic sequence is overlain by a massive porphyritic andesite with a blocky flow-brecciated base and top. Contrast the characteristics of this unit with the basalts below.

An excellent panoramic view can be seen from the summit of Yoadcastle. To the north the low, craggy exposures of the Eskdale Granite contrast strongly with the impressive volcanic peaks of the central fells to the north-east and the low undulating drift covered coastal area underlain by Triassic St. Bees Sandstone, stretching northwards from the Esk estuary.

Locality 6 (SD 15659508). Across the flattish area to the south-west of Yoadcastle are exposures of an acid nodular ignimbrite and an overlying white-weathered dacite. The latter   is the 'Great Whinscale Rhyolite' first recognised by Firman (1957) as a widespread marker horizon. These are the most south-westerly exposures of these deposits which will be further examined on Itinerary 11 to Harter Fell. The lower unit is a feldspar-rich tuff containing in its upper part, spherical , siliceous nodules. A eutaxitic texture is present locally in the nodule-free areas. The dacite is dark grey, splintery and strongly foliated and succeeds the nodular ignimbrite without intervening tuffs (compare with sequence on Harter Fell, itinerary 11).

Locality 7 (SD 15859485). Continue south-eastwards, crossing several lava flows to the clastic deposits forming the end of this range (exposures near Robert Cross). Well-bedded, medium to coarse tuff with normal grading and parallel stratification is interbedded with a thin, eutaxitic textured ignimbrite.

A return to the car park can be made from here by following the grassy slopes and Hell Beck north-east to meet the track at Devoke Water.

ITINERARY 8

Upper Eskdale to Scar Lathing and Silverybield Crags

D. Millward, British Geological Survey

1:25,000 map NY 20 or Outdoor Leisure Map 6
This full-day excursion on open fellside examines mainly thick, compound, basalt lavas of the Birker Fell Formation of the Borrowdale Volcanic Group (BVG) in Upper Eskdale. The route is long (c. 9-10km), but not arduous being, in part, along well-marked paths and ascending no more than 400m. The geology and route (Localities 1-9) are given in Figure 28.

The excursion starts form Brotherilkeld (NY 21250140), reached either from Eskdale Green via Boot, or from Ambleside over Wrynose and Hard Knott passes. Use of the passes is not advised during winter conditions. There is sufficient parking space for a small number of cars at various places between Whahouse Bridge (NY 20370089) and the eastern side of the cattle grid at (NY 21330108).

Follow the well-marked path from Brotherilkeld north-east along the east bank of the Esk for 2.5km. The route is initially along the edge of a channelled river terrace. The white crags on the hilltop to the west are of Eskdale Granite, the upper surface of which dips shallowly north-east beneath the Esk valley. An imposing view of the crags of Hard Knott is seen to the east. North-east from the second stone wall (NY 21940235), some 1.5km from Brotherilkeld, numerous grass-covered alluvial fans spread out from the small streams draining Hard Knott. To the left the imposing Heron Crags have significant scree deposits. The BVG is exposed at intervals along the streams. In the small waterfall (NY 22480300) good flow-jointing is present in andesite.

Locality 1 (NY 22610333). Some 360m upstream from the waterfall porphyritic andesite is cut by a 2m wide grey-green basalt dyke trending 110°. The fresh surface of the country rock, a porphyritic andesite, has a distinct brownish tinge and a fine hornfelsed texture. It contains much microcrystalline biotite and lies within the contact metamorphic aureole of the Eskdale Granite. A further 80-100m upstream, bedded tuff overlies the andesite.

Locality 2 (NY 22630370). Cross Lingcove Beck at the old packhorse bridge (NY 22730362) and examine rocks in the banks of the Esk 80-180m upstream. A thin sequence of ignimbrite and bedded tuff overlies porphyritic andesite. The ignimbrite has a good eutaxitic texture. The tuff is fine-grained and although much is parallel-laminated some shallow-angle cross-stratification with small dune-like structures and lapilli sags is present. It is possible that these beds were deposited from pyroclastic surges.

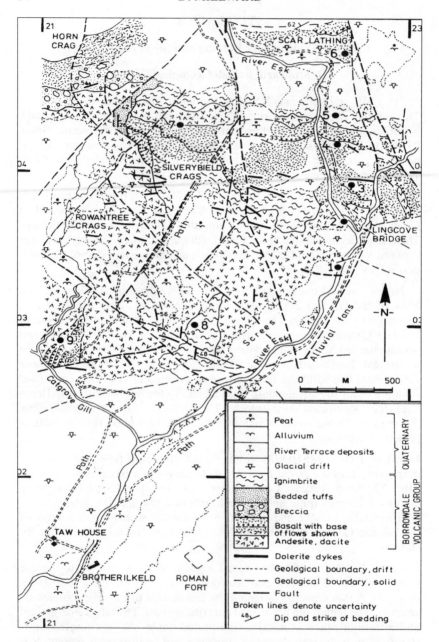

Figure 28. The Borrowdale Volcanics of Upper Eskdale.

Locality 3 Throstle Garth (NY 227039). Exposed on the spur between the Esk and Lingcove Beck are aphyric basalts. The hillside is well-featured and the rocks show much alternation between massive basalt channel-fills and clinkery, often highly amgydaloidal, flow breccias. This unit contains sparse pseudomorphs after olivine. In the small crag at NY 22720396 careful examination reveals a 2m wide dolerite dyke cutting the basalt in a W-E direction. The vertical dyke is identified by its coarser texture.

Locality 4 (NY 22680417). Thin, laminated tuff containing small slump folds is interbedded with the basalt sequence. The top of the underlying basalt is clinkery with intra-clast cavities filled with fine-grained sedimentary rock.

Locality 5 Throstlehow Crag (NY 22530441). Succeeding the basalts to the right of the well-marked path is a coarse, eutaxitic, dacitic ignimbrite.

Locality 6 Scar Lathing (NY 226048). Basalts, similar to those on Throstle Garth, form this prominent feature. Many rapid lateral and vertical alterations, from massive material to amygdaloidal and clinkery breccia, occur with only local interbeds of tuff. The basaltic rocks display features that are typical of compound lava flows; thick accumulations of lava erupted over considerable periods of time, at slow rates of effusion, building up a complex of channels and levées.

At the top of Scar Lathing a fine view of the Scafell range is to be seen. To the west in the imposing Cam Spout Crags massive ignimbrite dips from left to right and forms part of the Scafell syncline. At this juncture a return to Brotherilkeld may be made by retracing the route. For those prepared to cross the Esk (with care) either above the waterfalls at NY 22500459 or to the west of Scar Lathing at 22030485, a return can be made along the well-marked path (Figure 28) via Silverybield Crags and Catcove Beck to Taw House, perhaps examining the following exposures.

Locality 7 Silverybield Crags (NY 217042). Careful examination of the sequence here reveals that the ignimbrite (previously seen at Locality 5) and basalt (seen at Localities 3 and 4) are separated by a thin dacite having a blocky, flow-brecciated upper surface. The features of the basalts can be re-examined and the sequence traced westwards to where it terminated abruptly against bedded tuff. The main dip on Silverybield Crags is to the north, but the tuff dips eastward. The basalt, dacite and ignimbrite fill an original topographic depression.

Locality 8 North-east of Brock Crag (NY 21800300). A further steep contact, marked by abundant quartz veins, is exposed here with eutaxitic ignimbrite abutting porphyritic andesite.

Locality 9 (NY 211028). In these crags several thin porphyritic basalt flows with intercalated tuff are exposed. Clinkery breccias cap each flow, but compare and contrast these *simple* flows with the *compound* ones seen previously.

ITINERARY 9

Cockley Beck-Grey Friar

E.W. Johnson, British Geological Survey

1:25,000 map NY20 or Outdoor Leisure Map 6

The purpose of this excursion is to examine the lower part of the Borrowdale Volcanic Group (BVG) succession on the southern limb of the Wrynose Anticline. The succession is dominated by andesitic and dacitic lavas that show a variety of morphological features. Lithologically distinctive pyroclastic rocks within the sequence are useful stratigraphic markers, and intercalated epiclastic tuff units illustrate erosional and depositional processes.

The whole-day excursion involves 5km of walking, mostly over rough fellside with few defined paths, and a climb of almost 600m. Cars can be parked on the roadside between Cockley Beck Bridge (NY 246017) and the cattle grid at NY 257020. Alternatively, the excursion can be concluded at the top of Wrynose Pass (NY 277027) where roadside parking is also available (Figure 29).

Locality 1 (NY 24970172). The Duddon Valley east of Cockley Beck coincides with the axis of the east-northeast plunging Wrynose Anticline, and the Eskdale-Hardknott-Wrynose Fault. The gently dipping strata on the northern limb of the fold are seen to the north-east on Cold Pike (NY 264035) and Little Stand (NY 250034). The steeply dipping southern limb of the fold exposes 1500m of strata between Cockley Beck (NY 247016) and the summit of Grey Friar (NY 260004).

The small crag (NY 24970172) exposes debris-flow breccias (lahars), which are the lowest beds in the area. The matrix-supported, heterolithic breccia is ill-sorted and contains angular to subrounded clasts. Intercalated thin-bedded and laminated tuff indicates fluviatile deposition. Near the centre of the crag a breccia dyke cuts the debris-flow. The comparable lithology of both dyke and flow suggests that the dyke originated by dewatering of the breccia.

Locality 2 (NY 24960151). Lithologically uniform andesite, with a regular joint-set, crops out on the south side of the plantation and is interpreted as an irregular, intrusive plug. Although its contact with the debris-flow breccia and the overlying ignimbrite is not exposed, the cross-cutting relationship can be deduced from the surrounding exposures. Similar plugs occur to the south-west.

The andesitic ignimbrite exposed immediately on the south-east side of the fence, is crystal-rich and has a good eutaxitic texture. Abundant plagioclase and euhedral garnet make it lithologically distinctive. The unit is

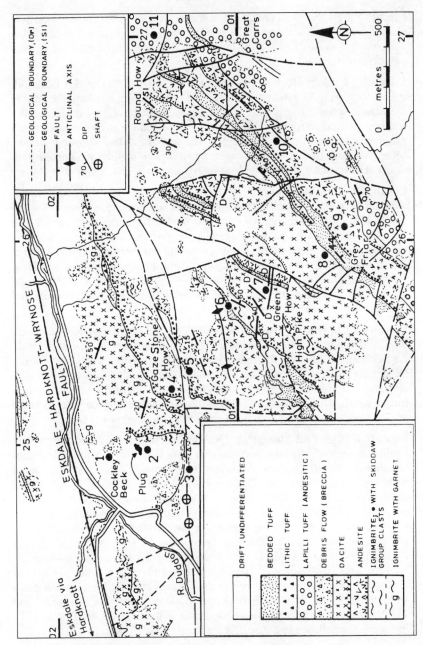

Figure 29. The Borrowdale Volcanics of the Cockley Beck-Grey Friar area.

a local stratigraphic marker that extends into Eskdale, a distance of 6km (see also itinerary 20, Locality 1). The ignimbrite is a compound unit; following the crop S, towards Locality 3, individual flow units are separated by thin pyroclastic surge beds.

Locality 3 Cockley Beck Copper Mine (NY 24870128). Cockley Beck Gill is cut along an E-W trending fault. A level has been driven along the fault in the stream, where there is a 0.1m wide zone of calcite veining in the sheared and hematised country rock. Small spoil tips beside the stream contain much gangue calcite with traces of chalcopyrite and secondary copper minerals. More extensive tips occur to the west where the vein has been worked from shafts. The track on the north side of the stream leads to Locality 4.

Locality 4 Gaze Stone How (NY 252014). A greenish-grey, basic andesite with a rubbly, flow-brecciated top wedges out on Gaze Stone How. Less than 1m of bedded tuff separates it from the top of the underlying dacite. The pink-weathered dacite lava is plagioclase-phyric. Sparse garnet xenocrysts are identified by small spherical pits on weathered surfaces. Northeastwards a prominent slack defines the irregular, flow-brecciated top of the lava. Locally an ignimbrite is preserved in hollows. The ignimbrite is lithic-rich; many of the fragments are arkosic sandstone, siltstone and mudstone derived from the subvolcanic Skiddaw Group basement.

Locality 5 Copthwaite How (NY 25440128). The sparsely pyroxene-phyric basic andesite at Locality 4 is also exposed south of the Cockley Beck Fault. At the base of the crag the massive central part of the lava flow is seen. Higher on the crag a weak flow-foliation is developed with flow-folds with amplitudes up to 2m. The rubbly, flow-brecciated top of the lava is exposed further south. This 75m thick lava flow has an unusually wide outcrop south of Copthwaite How produced by an eastward-plunging, minor fold.

Locality 6 High Peat Stock (NY 256011). A few metres of bedded tuff and lapilli tuff separate the lava from the overlying ignimbrite. A prominent joint set, dipping 20° to the north-northwest is developed in the white weathered ignimbrite which, towards the top, is crudely bedded. Locally the ignimbrite has a poorly developed eutaxitic texture and contains fiamme up to 30cm long. The most distinctive character is the abundance of lithic clasts it contains, including various andesite types and rhyodacite, but most commonly arkosic sandstone, siltstone and mudstone derived from the Skiddaw Group basement. Following the outcrop southwestwards, ESE trending dolerite dykes cut the ignimbrite 20-30m from the enclosure wall. The lithic-rich ignimbrite is a distinctive marker on Grey Friar; it is the highest bed of the Great Whinscale Member that has a widespread outcrop between Eskdale and Duddon Valley (see itinerary 7 and 11). Northwards there is a splendid panorama of the central Lake District Fells including Sca Fell, Sca Fell Pike, Esk Pike and Crinkle Crags.

Leave the enclosed ground by the gate in the recently erected fence.

Locality 7 Green How (NY 257008). South of the enclosure wall, pink-weathered, porphyritic dacite lava is well-exposed alongside the collapsed wall that extends up the fellside. Near its base the lava has a weak flow-foliation. Patchy epidotisation is visible in hand-specimen. Almost 100m from the junction with the enclosure wall an ill-defined gully trending 100° marks the course of a dolerite dyke. Follow the dyke east to a prominent trending grassy slack and continue south along the slack for about 250m to where it is intersected by a southeasterly trending minor fault which is followed to locality 8.

Locality 8 Brow Side Fell (NY 259004). A good, blocky flow-breccia is present at the top of the dacite lava. Interstices between the angular blocks are filled with laminated tuff. Overlying the dacite lava is 10m of eutaxitic, andesitic lapilli tuff. Fiamme are concentrated near the base and non-vesiculated lapilli are inversely graded. The succeeding thin, bedded tuff is cut out along strike by an erosion surface. These fluvial deposits indicate a sub-aerial environment. The succeeding tuff is mostly in thin, parallel beds. Medium and thick graded beds are present near the base; some have discordant bases and others cross-sets. Continue uphill towards the summit of Grey Friar.

Locality 9 Grey Friar (NY 261004). At the summit, protruding through the cover of frost-shattered blocks, there are small exposures of andesite lava and interbeds of tuff. The plagioclase and pyroxene-phyric andesite to the north of the summit cairn contains epidote-filled amygdales towards its top. The succeeding 10-12m of bedded tuff includes thick beds of lapilli tuff of probable airfall origin. Above the tuff is a greenish-weathered, sparsely pyroxene-phyric basalt. These lavas are locally the youngest strata of the lower part of the Birker Fell Formation and are overlain by the Whorneyside Tuff (Branney, 1988a). The boundary marks a fundamental change in volcanic style. The Whorneyside Tuff, and andesitic lapilli tuff, can be examined 150m southwest of the summit; a eutaxitic texture is present at the base.

The panorama from the summit includes: to the north, Harter Fell and the central fells of the Lake District; to the east, Swirl How, where the white-weathered crop of the rhyodacitic ignimbrite (?Airy's Bridge Formation) can be traced south-west to Little Pikes and Dow Crag; and to the south-west, the Duddon Valley, its estuary and the Irish Sea.

The main purpose of the field trip fulfilled, this is a suitable point to conclude the excursion. The energetic hill walker can use the height gained to advantage; the summits of Swirl How, Wetherlam, Coniston Old Man and Dow Crag all lie within a reasonable distance. The remaining localities can be visited by enthusiasts. The recommended way to return to Cockley Beck is to take the footpath towards Locality 10 and descend either Snowdrift Slack or follow the course of Troughton Gill.

Locality 10 Black Sprouts (NY 264007). The flow-brecciated top of the youngest lava exposed is unusual in that voids are present on the weathered surface between the blocks. In the bedded tuff underlying the lava, a 1.4m breccia shows good reverse grading and concentration of angular blocks towards the top, approximately 10m above the base.

Locality 11 NE of Little Carrs (NY 27000145 to 27150162). The upper part of the Whorneyside Tuff is well-exposed near the 692m spot height. The coarse grained, andesitic ignimbrite contains plagioclase and pyroxene crystals and abundant non-vesiculated essential andesitic lapilli. Scattered accessory lithic blocks of older volcanic rocks up to 20cm x 5cm are distinguished by recessed weathering. A weak eutaxitic texture is present and the uppermost part is crudely stratified parallel to bedding in the overlying tuff. The top of the Whorneyside Tuff is marked by an irregular erosion surface and is overlain by bedded tuff or by rhyodacitic tuff units which are correlated with the Airy's Bridge Formation. The bedded, andesitic tuff is graded and there is a decrease in bed thickness upwards.

The irregular contact with the overlying Airy's Bridge Formation lies within 10m of the path (see 1:25,000 map) and can be examined over a distance of 150m. White weathered, weakly bedded tuff occurs locally at the base. The ill-defined bedding and thin beds of accretionary lapilli suggest interplay between airfall and pyroclastic surge activity.

The path bends to the north and follows the crop of the Whorneyside Tuff onto Wet Side Edge. The cairn at NY 27450213 provides a vantage point to appreciate the view: east to Little Langdale with the Greenburn Valley and the long-disused workings associated with the copper mine; south to Wetherlam and the Coniston Fells; and west along Wrynose Bottom to Harter Fell and Hardknott Pass. From the cairn the path left provides a steep descent to Wrynose Pass.

ITINERARY 10

Hard Knott, Eskdale

D. Millward, British Geological Survey

1:25,000 map NY 20 or Outdoor Leisure Map 6

Up to a full day can be spent examining the sequence on Hard Knott, the entire route being over open fell with a 6km walk and 450m ascent. The excursion demonstrates various aspects of the volcanic geology of the Birker Fell Formation and also a sequence of later, acid pyroclastic deposits which have a steep, unconformable relationship with the earlier lava pile.

The excursion starts on the west side of Hard Knott; location of car parking facilities is given in itinerary 8. The geology and route with localities 1-8 are shown in Figure 30.

Approximately 100m uphill from the cattle grid (NY 21330108), and to the left is a path and gate leading to the fellside. From here climb diagonally uphill to the crags of Bell Stand and locality 1.

Locality 1 Bell Stand (NY 21570136). At the base of the crag is a pink-weathered, pale grey, vitric tuff with abundant feldspar and small, generally euhedral, garnet. It also has a good eutaxitic texture. This ignimbrite is the important marker horizon seen previously in itinerary 9 (Locality 2).

The garnet-bearing ignimbrite is overlain by a thin, highly amygdaloidal andesite and a thick sparsely garnetiferous dacite flow which crop out across the plateau area on which the Roman Fort is built. At this point the opportunity can be taken to examine the remains of the fort and to enjoy the views of the once-forested Eskdale. From here it is also possible to see the crag and bench features on Border End, produced respectively by blocky andesite and thin, tuff interbeds.

Locality 2 (NY 22350161). Some 450m east-northeast of the fort, the top of the garnet-bearing dacite is well-exposed. Hollows in the irregular, flow-brecciated top to this lava are filled with thin-bedded and laminated, coarse to fine-grained tuff. Small-scale tough cross-bedding and imbricated rip-up clasts indicate fluviatile deposition. On the small dip slope above the crag top (NY 22380162) is a thin ignimbrite containing abundant small clasts of siltstone and sandstone of Skiddaw Group origin.

Border End can be climbed by walking north from Locality 2 along the steep bench feature observing, along the way, the irregular top to the lava flow (exposed in the crag) and filling of hollows by laminated tuff (exposed at the top of the crag and on the bench). On reaching the more level parts of this bench (approximately NY 22410197) the main crags can be ascended safely.

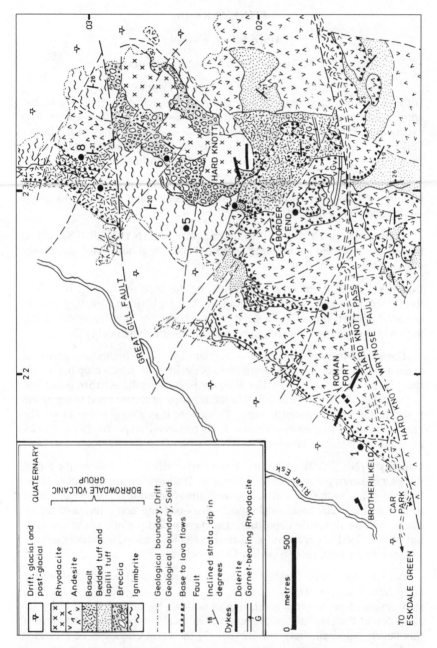

Figure 30. The Borrowdale Volcanics in the Hard Knott area, Eskdale.

Locality 3 Border End and Raven Crag (NY 228018). Capping the sequence here are two andesite flows that show features described as typical of composite lava flows (Allen *et al.*, 1987). Each flow consists of a massive to flow-jointed, feldspar-phyric acid andesite centre, with a more basic top and base. The interfaces between the compositional zones have viscosity contrast structures including cumulose margins and balls or pillows at the basal interface and complex interlayering, commonly with folding, at the upper. These features and blocky flow-breccias with fine, laminated internal sediment can be seen.

The summit of Hard Knott, between its southern limit (NY 22680228 to 23230203) and Great Gill (NY 23000280), exposes a sequence of 260m of rhyodacitic ignimbrite, 170m of breccias and 50m of sparsely garnetiferous rhyodacite. This rests with steep unconformity on the lavas seen so far and is correlated with the thick ignimbrites of the Airy's Bridge Formation of the Central Fells (Oliver, 1961).

Locality 4 (NY 22870217). Here the steep unconformity can be examined in a small crag. White-weathered rhyodacitic lava and ignimbrite breccias are separated from the older, andesite lavas by a uniform breccia of andesite clasts interpreted as a talus deposit.

Locality 5 Eskdale Needle (NY 22810241). The ignimbrites, representing valley or caldera-fill, can be examined at many localities, for example at Eskdale Needle. The ignimbrite is pale-weathered, flinty, grey, poorly feldspar-phyric and has a prominent eutaxitic texture. The lower part of the sequence (NY 22300263) locally consists of many flow units, from 3cm to 2m thick, each showing grading of fiamme and changes in the abundance of lithic clasts; some are separated by thin interbeds of laminated tuff. From Eskdale Needle the Scafell, Esk Pike and Bowfell range is magnificently displayed in good visibility.

Locality 6 (NY 23170254). The breccias are well-exposed on the west side of Hard Knott where they are bedded in units 2-30m thick. The lower, thicker part of each unit is massive and composed of clast-supported, angular to subrounded cobbles and boulders of rhyodacite with some blocks up to 4m. The upper part is variably parallel-bedded volcanic sandstone and conglomerate. The upper surface of the breccias is generally planar and gives rise to good crag and bench featuring; locally, as at Locality 6, there are scours and channels filled with reworked detritus. These breccias were probably produced in a similar manner to the the sediment flows generated during the 1982 eruption of Mount St. Helens, where rivers of boulders dammed the Toutle river (Harrison and Fritz, 1982).

Locality 7 Great Gill Head Crag (NY 23000294). North of the Great Gill Fault (Figure 30) the Birker Fell Formation is once again exposed and here the base of a lava flow is visible from the small bench. Bedded, coarse tuff crops out on the bench, but in the crag above about 1m from the bench is the basal flow breccia to a pyroxene-plagioclase-phyric basic andesite. The breccia clasts are pillow-shaped and the intervening coarse tuff is homogeneous and unbedded. Eruption onto a water-saturated substrate caused boiling of the interstitial water and the subsequent injection of sediment into the base of the flow. Cavities higher in this breccia were later filled by laminated and cross-laminated tuff, and in their upper parts by chalcedony.

Locality 8 (NY 23160300). 150m north-east of Great Gill Head Crag are crags of dark green-grey aphyric basalt. Rapid variations are present from massive channel-fills to highly amygdaloidal and clinkery breccias. Compare the breccia clast shapes with those of the blocky andesites on Border End for example. An explanation of the flow morphology of these basalts is given in itinerary 8.

Return to the car by either retracing the route or, if time allows, continuing the walk north along the ridge to Lingcove Beck (NY 233043) and following the well marked path down Lingcove Beck and the Esk to Brotherilkeld (45 mins-1 hour). In good visibility, fine views of upper Eskdale and the Sca Fell range can be appreciated during this walk.

ITINERARY 11

Harter Fell, Dunnerdale

D. Millward, British Geological Survey

1:25,000 map SD29 or Outdoor Leisure Map 6
This is a half to three-quarter day excursion that involves a round-trip of about 5km and the ascent of Harter Fell, some 470m above the Duddon valley. The terrain is rough, steep and, in general, not along marked paths. The Birker Fell Formation here contains important widespread marker horizons and the summit provides a vantage point for the magnificent scenery in this area. The geology is shown in Figure 31.

The start is made from the car park in the Dunnerdale Forest (SD 23509955) some 200m north of Birks Bridge, and is reached along the Duddon valley road from either Broughton-in-Furness via Ulpha, or Ambleside via Wrynose Pass. In general the sequence is poorly exposed and intensely faulted in the valley bottom, but cleaved porphyritic andesite is exposed beside the road. The excursion commences at Brandy Crag (SD 226990).

Brandy Crag is reached by following the forestry road from the car park. A clearing with many enclosure walls is located west of Birks and hereabouts (SD 22909918) a path leads uphill to open out into a well-marked, wide, fire-break within tall conifers. A small clearing after some

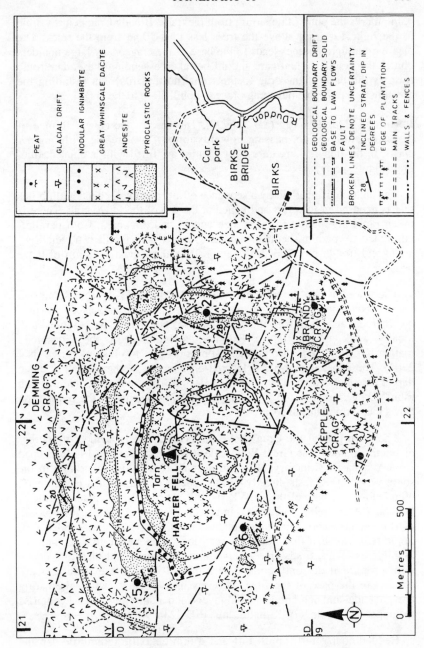

Figure 31. The Borrowdale Volcanics from Birks, Dunnerdale, to Harter Fell.

450m marks the point of departure from the track. Brandy Crag is just visible to the right, towering above the trees less than 100m from the track. The clearing through the trees leads to the base of the crag. Many large boulders clutter the crag base and care should be taken ascending these. The route follows the base of the crag to the right (northwards). On rounding the precipitous part of the main crag proceed uphill close to the crag.

Locality 1 Brandy Crag (SD 226990). The base of the crag is formed of massive acid andesite, passing upwards into a flow breccia with angular clasts. In the upper 1-2m, intra-clast cavities are filled with laminated, fine-grained tuff.

The andesite is overlain by a sequence of tuff and interbedded ignimbrites that is exposed in the crest and bench at the top of the lower crag. There is much rapid alternation in grain size and in bed thickness, from parallel-laminated to medium-bedded, medium-grained and lapilli tuff. Shallow-angle and trough cross-bedding demonstrate the fluviatile origin of these beds.

The lower of two ignimbrites within the sequence is located some two metres above the andesite. It is approximately 5m thick and has a very pale weathered crust. It is recognised by sparse, but distinctive nodules and, locally, weak eutaxitic fabric. This nodular ignimbrite is the widespread marker horizon mapped from Yoadcastle (itinerary 7) to Pike of Blisco (NY 2704). The upper ignimbrite is located on the crest of the crag. It is much darker than the lower and is probably andesitic. There are many fiamme with rapid changes in size and abundance indicating pulsing of the pyroclastic flows that formed this deposit.

The main part of the Crag above the bedded tuff is formed of another distinctive marker (the Great Whinscale Rhyolite of Firman, 1957) mapped from Yoadcastle (Itinerary 7) to Little Stand (NY 2403). Note that to the south-west 'GWR' rests directly on the nodular ignimbrite that is seen here, 40m below. The base of the ' GWR' is well-exposed on the southern side of the crag (SD 22469894) where a thin breccia of angular to subangular blocks of flow-banded and flow-folded dacite conformably overlies bedded tuff. Some tight isoclinal flow folds are seen locally above the breccia, but this rapidly passes up, firstly into finely foliated material and then into dacite with prominent discontinuous, fine joints. Both of these structures are parallel to the base of the flow. Strongly banded dacite with alternating amygdaloidal and non-amygdaloidal layers, and a thin flow-breccia comprise the upper part of the 'GWR' in this area (SD 22389902).

Bedded coarse tuff, lapilli tuff and a thin eutaxitic ignimbrite cap the 'GWR' and are overlain by andesite flows.

Locality 2 Dropping Crag (SD 22509945). This impressive crag and bench feature is reached by continuing in a northerly direction from Brandy Crag. The precipitous crags expose flows of highly porphyritic andesite with blocky flow breccias at base and top. However, it is the interbeds of tuff and breccia that are worthy of careful examination. Stratigraphically this sequence lies below the andesite that forms the base of Brandy Crag (Locality 1), from which it is separated by faults along well-marked gullies.

The lowest 3-4m of the clastic sequence, filling the irregular surface to the underlying andesite, consists of laminated, medium to coarse-grained tuff, with low-angle cross-lamination. The rest of the sequence is of extremely heterogeneous, bedded, coarse-grained tuff and breccia. These are heterolithic, very poorly sorted and consist mainly of angular and non-vesicular clasts up to 30cm. Bedding is generally parallel but there are many faint, low-angle truncations and discontinuous laminae. Locally these are low amplitude dune-like structures and scattered bombs with underlying sags. These characteristics are typical of base-surges produced by the interaction of magma with water from an aquifer or lake.

Climb northwards through the nodular ignimbrite (eg. at SD 22359966) and the Great Whinscale dacite to the tarn located 150m north of the summit of Harter Fell.

Locality 3 Small tarn (SD 21889985). A few metres north of the small tarn is an excellent section through the nodular ignimbrite. Nodules are concentrated towards the top and in a 1.5m thick zone approximately 1.5m above the base of the unit. The central part contains sparse chloritic fiamme giving a weak eutaxitic texture. Near the tarn are bedded coarse tuffs and lapilli tuff. There is much parallel bedding with channelling and cross-lamination. The overlying 'GWR' shows very similar features to Locality 1.

Locality 4 Summit of Harter Fell (SD 21859971). The 'GWR' is overlain by thin, bedded tuff and two blocky andesites. The central parts of the flows are strongly jointed in the lowest part, passing up into a flow-banded and flow-folded middle section and into a blocky breccia with cavity fills of laminated fine-grained tuff at the top. Magnificent views of the scenery are to be had from this fine vantage point.

Descend the well-trodden path westwards from the summit, noting, just to the north side, about 80m from the summit, the superb flow-folds in the andesite. A further 70m downhill and to the left (south side) of the track the 'GWR' is locally, highly amygdaloidal (cf. Brandy Crag).

Locality 5 (SFD 21269989). About 600m from the summit a thick sequence of bedded coarse tuff forms a prominent bench. Note the top to the underlying blocky flow-brecciated andesite and the mantling of bedding over the irregular surface. From here follow topographic contours southwards to the prominent exposures at Locality 6.

Locality 6 (SD 21459930). At this locality examine the sedimentary structures comparing them with other features seen previously.

Locality 7 Kepple Crag (SD 219987). The descent to Kepple Crag marks a return to the forestry track which can be followed to the car park. The features are typical of blocky andesites. Flow breccia with internal sediment, flow-jointing and massive to flow-banded material are all well-displayed.

ITINERARY 12

Buckbarrow and Middle Fell, Wasdale

M. G. Petterson, British Geological Survey

1: 25,000 map NY 10 or Outdoor Leisure Map 6

This full day's trip to Wasdale provides the opportunity to study the lower part of the Borrowdale Volcanic Group (BVG) together with the southern part of the Ennerdale Granophyre. The full excursion is 6km long and involves a total climb of 600m. The terrain is rough and requires strenuous walking.

The starting point for the field trip is close to Greendale (NY 14350563) which is approximately 6km east of Gosforth, or 2km north-east of Nether Wasdale. There are two main parking areas - one is close to Buckbarrow Farm along the roadside (NY 138054) and the other adjacent to the confluence of Goat Gill with Wastwater (NY 157061). Parking spaces are limited, especially at the height of the tourist season.

Locality points are marked on the geological sketch map (Figure 32).

Locality 1 Buckbarrow Farm (NY 13540552). Just above the roadside, adjacent to the easternmost field, are a number of exposures of the Ennerdale Granophyre. The rock is a pink, medium-grained, leucocratic microgranite with a granular, "sugary", texture. Mafic crystals (chlorite after biotite), comprise a small proportion of the rock. It is fairly homogeneous in this area, though some exposures are riddled with quartz veins.

Localities 2 and 3 Buckbarrow Crags (NY 13540666 and 13630572). Climb up the steep fellside, adjacent to the outer fence of the easternmost field. At the top of the field note that outcrops of Ennerdale Granophyre are close to volcanic rocks, although the contact is not exposed. Climb east-northeast nearly to the top of a recent scree deposit - here the contact between the granophyre and the BVG is exposed. The contact is irregular, with apophyses of granophyre locally intruding the BVG. Contact metamorphism is minimal, though an increase in grain size in the volcanic rocks can be observed close to the junction.

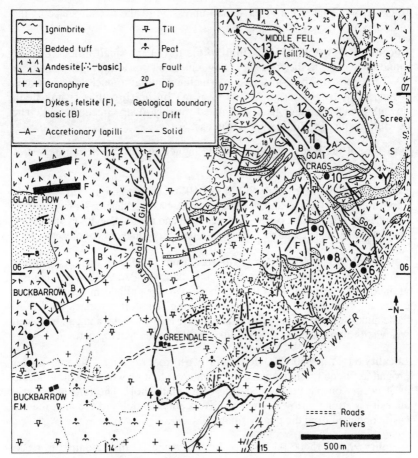

Figure 32. Geological map of Buckbarrow and Middle Fell, Wasdale.

The volcanic rocks here are predominantly feldspar-phyric andesite. They tend to be massive, with some flow-jointing.

Head eastwards to Locality 3 in a gully. Felsite and dolerite dykes are exposed near here; they cut both the BVG and the granophyre. The contact between the granophyre and the BVG can be followed eastwards along Buckbarrow Crags to Greendale Gill, or alternatively, return to Buckbarrow Farm by the same route.

Locality 4 (NY 14350530). A pleasant walk along Greendale Gill, about 400m south from Greendale Restaurant, leads to Locality 4 which provides an excellent viewpoint to the granophyre/BVG contact exposed on

Buckbarrow Crags. This gives some impression of the overall shape of the granophyre.

Locality 5 (NY 15080550). Climb to the top of the small hillock of pink granophyre close to the roadside. Only tens of metres to the north the darker BVG is exposed. The contact here is inclined and at a much lower altitude (80m) than Buckbarrow Crags (250m) indicating that it has been downthrown by a major fault, orientated roughly along Greendale Gill. The downthrow on the fault is some 170m east.

Some felsite dykes intrude the BVG higher on the fellside north-west of locality 5.

Locality 6 Wastwater shore (NY 15700606). On the shore of Wastwater are exposures of pyroxene and feldspar-phyric, basic andesite. Note how this becomes increasingly brecciated between here and the road, and how increasing amounts of laminated sediment are interspersed between blocks of breccia.

Locality 7 (NY 156060). Cross the road from Locality 6 and examine the exposures of bedded tuff adjacent to the roadside. Parallel-bedded, coarse-grained tuff alternates with thinner beds of finer grained material. Rip-up clasts are evidence of sedimentary reworking. The tuff separates the lower, basic andesite from an upper, feldspar-phyric acid andesite, and can be traced westwards along strike, though faults complicate the outcrop pattern.

Locality 8 (NY 15550608). Head north-west from Locality 7 onto the higher ground until you reach a small quarry which at first may be difficult to locate as it occurs on the north-west side of a small knoll. The feldspar-phyric andesite is strongly flow-jointed at this locality. Samples of the andesite are easily obtained from the quarry floor.

Locality 9 (NY 154063). A steep climb of some 100m is required to reach Locality 9 where a felsite dyke trending NNW-SSE intrudes the volcanic sequence. It is fine-grained, has a vitreous texture and breaks with a splintery, conchoidal fracture. It commonly has a banded, planar fabric parallel to the dyke margins.

Follow the dyke upwards to a bench exposing a sequence of bedded pyroclastic rocks. These are about 6m thick and consist, from bottom to top, of andesitic bedded tuff, a thin, pale grey to white-weathered ignimbrite, and an upper unit dominated by weakly bedded, coarse tuff with lapilli and thin interbeds of well-laminated, finer grained tuff.

Closely examine the basal contact of the pyroclastic sequence where it overlies a flow-brecciated andesite. This can be followed around the hillside, the best exposures being towards the west.

Locality 10 Lower Goat Crags (NY 155065). From Locality 9, cross Goat Gill and ascend some 100m. Here thin, grey, parallel-bedded tuff and acidic ignimbrite unconformably overlie the lower sequence of lavas. The unconformity can be followed eastwards, downhill, progressively overstepping older lavas and tuff.

The ignimbrite weathers to a white or pink colour, and is commonly eutaxitic with lenticular, chloritized fiamme that have weathered to form hollows on the rock surfaces. The fiamme are set in a leucocratic, granular, unsorted groundmass. Note the generally low angle of dip of the eutaxitic fabric in the ignimbrite.

Locality 11 Goat Crags (NY 154067). From Locality 10 head upwards following the junction between the crags and scree. Climb some 100m until a bench feature is reached. Fiamme are spectacularly exposed on some of the fallen boulders. Note the sub-horizontal dip to the eutaxitic fabric in the ignimbrite of the crags. Towards the eastern part of the bench several thin (60cm) layers of accretionary lapilli tuff are exposed. Individual lapilli are ovate to circular in cross-section and up to 1cm in diameter. Accretionary lapilli occur at several stratigraphical horizons within the ignimbrite sequence.

Locality 12 (NY 153069 to 155069). Cross the scree and continue the ascent, following the crags northwards. Parts of this section are dangerous and care must be taken. Keep to the base of the crags and avoid climbing them. Work towards the summit of Middle Fell stopping en route at Locality 12 to examine further exposures of the ignimbrite.

The ignimbrite at Locality 12 is heterogeneous, consisting of bedded, coarse tuff, unsorted breccia, and eutaxitic-textured rock similar to the lower exposures (Localities 10,11). The overall impression is that ignimbrite becomes progressively more heterogeneous higher in the succession.

Locality 13 Top of the Middle Fell (NY 151072). Head north-west from 12 to the top of Middle Fell observing the numerous exposures of the upper ignimbrite *en route*. Inliers of the underlying andesitic sequence may be seen in this section, indicating that the ignimbrite forms only a superficial layer (Figure 33).

Several ignimbrite beds form bench features striking approximately south-east. The top of Middle Fell is an example. The highest exposed part of the ignimbrite crops out at this locality and consists of 5m or so of bedded tuff. This varies from coarse to fine-grained, and contains some accretionary lapilli. The composition is dominantly andesitic, though there is a thin layer of fine-grained, pink, acid material which is either a tuff or a felsite sill.

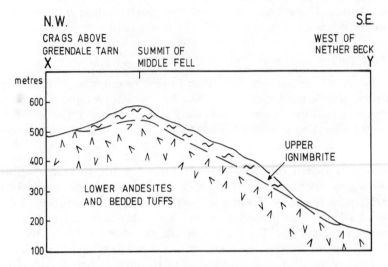

Fig. 33. Sketch section across Middle Fell showing the relationship between the upper ignimbrites and lower andesites (vertical and horizontal scales equal).

From the top of Middle Fell a spectacular panorama is revealed which includes the red dacite of Seatallan, the darker andesites of High Fell and Yewbarrow, and the more dramatic higher fells of Great Gable, Sca Fell, the Screes, Black Coombe, Haycock and Red Pike.

The descent into Wasdale requires care, especially if descending directly to Wast Water. A more leisurely, and safer, but much longer, route follows the path to Greendale (marked on the 1:25,000 map).

ITINERARY 13

Holehouse Gill

E.W. Johnson, British Geological Survey

1:25,000 sheet SD19 or Outdoor Leisure Map 6
The purpose of this half-day excursion is to examine the marine strata of the Holehouse Gill Formation in the type section, and its relationship with the volcanic rocks. The Holehouse Gill Formation comprises the only marine strata within the Borrowdale Volcanic Group. Stratigraphically it is in the upper part of the volcanic succession. It represents a brief, localized marine incursion within an otherwise subaerial sequence. It is located within the centre of a rapidly subsiding, volcano-tectonic basin. Silty mudstone within the formation has yielded acritarch assemblages that indicate an early Caradocian age (Molyneux, 1988). Microgranite dykes, mineralisation and associated workings of the disused Ulpha Copper Mine will also be seen. This itinerary combines readily with itinerary 14 providing a whole day in the lower Duddon Valley. The geology and localities are shown in Figure 34.

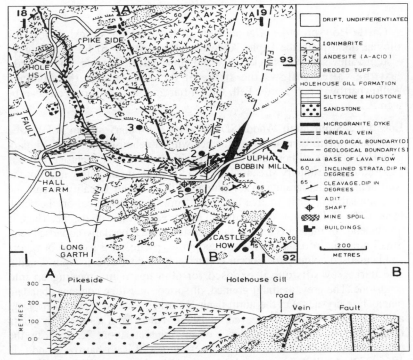

Figure 34. Geological map of the Holehouse Gill area, Dunnerdale.

Less than 3km of walking in rough pasture land is required. The stream section is extremely hazardous, great care is required descending the steep banks and the going alongside the stream is rough. The stream has a large catchment area and rises rapidly in wet weather. IT IS DANGEROUS TO ATTEMPT THIS EXCURSION WHEN THE STREAM IS IN SPATE.

Parking alongside the narrow road is difficult; space for 1 or 2 cars can found near Ulpha Bobbin Mill (SD 190925) and immediately east of the disused shaft (Locality 5). Alternatively, vehicles can be left near Ulpha Bridge (SD 196930), 1km to the north-east.

Locality 1 Castle How (SD 19839200). Thin-bedded tuff exposed on the north side of the hill contains low-angle bedding discordances, gentle flexures and folds that are indicators of syndepositional deformation; channels and cross-bedding confirm subaerial, fluviatile erosion and deposition. An interbedded andesite lava forms the knoll of Castle How; it rests unconformably on thin-bedded and laminated tuff and the basal part is characterised by blocky jointing. It is porphyritic with plagioclase and chloritised mafic phenocrysts. A pink microgranite dyke cuts the sequence on the south-east side of the hill; the dyke is likely to be early Devonian in age.

Castle How provides a good view of the Duddon Valley. Across the alluvial flood plain the Ulpha Andesites (Mitchell, 1956) form the rugged eastern valley side with Stickle Pike and Great Stickle beyond. To the north-east the valley follows the strike of the beds and in the distance Wallowbarrow Crag, Harter Fell, Grey Friar and the Coniston Fells can be seen.

Locality 2 Stonegarth Wood (SD 187924). A tributary stream is followed from Bobbin Hill Lane to its confluence with Holehouse Gill. Cleaved, dark grey Holehouse Gill Formation siltstone with scattered plagioclase crystals is exposed in the tributary stream 40m from the road. Immediately north of the confluence a microgranite dyke, similar to that seen at Locality 1, cuts the silty mudstone. Thirty metres upstream from the confluence, on the south bank of the Gill, there is a level driven south-west in silty mudstone. There is no evidence of mineralisation in the mudstone in the partially-collapsed adit. Small amounts of chalcopyrite, arsenopyrite, pyrite, in a gangue of quartz and hematised country rock occur on the spoil tip downstream from the adit. The dark grey siltstone is exposed for 60m upstream, passing up into sandstone. The grey, medium-grained, ill-sorted sandstone contains abundant plagioclase crystals. On the north bank, a further 50m upstream, there is an adit, driven north-west in cleaved mudstone. Apart from a little vein quartz in the spoil tip there is no evidence of any mineralisation. Scramble up the north bank of the stream to the south-west corner of Rainsbarrow Wood (SD 18669252). An ill-defined track leads to Locality 3.

Locality 3 (SD 185927) Acid andesite lavas, the Ulpha Andesites of Mitchell (1956) and Firman (1957), crop out north-east of Holehouse Gill. A well-defined break in slope indicates the margin of the flow. Near the contact flow-joints, aligned parallel to the flow margin, are present. The acid andesite contains abundant plagioclase phenocrysts. The abrupt termination of the Ulpha Andesite against the younger portions of the Holehouse Gill Formation indicates penecontemporaneous sedimentation and eruption of the lava flow. The contact is unexposed and therefore its nature is not known with certainty. The generalised section (Figure 34) suggests that the lava is filling depressions in an intraformational erosion surface. Head south-west towards the confluence of Holehouse Gill and Tongue Beck (SD 18299260)

Locality 4 Holehouse Gill (SD 18299260 to 18189306). Strongly cleaved, dark grey silty mudstone is exposed at the confluence. The mudstone has yielded acritarch assemblages that indicate an early Caradocian age for the marine strata. No macrofossils have been found in the mudstone. Upstream, Holehouse Gill follows the course of a minor fault with downthrow to the west. Continue upstream for 80m to where the fault juxtaposes silty mudstone on the east bank against sandstone. The fault zone is 1m wide where it is exposed in the stream. The poorly bedded sandstone has a weak, parallel lamination and thin, siltstone interbeds indicating a northerly dip. The sandstone is mostly medium-grained, but some coarse-grained beds with siltstone rip-up clasts are present. Circumnavigate the gorge below the waterfall. Sandstone with siltstone interbeds is exposed in the meander above the waterfall; the sandstone is thin to medium-bedded and much of the siltstone is parallel-laminated and clearly demonstrates the dip direction. When viewed along strike to the north-east these beds must abut the Ulpha Andesites seen at Locality 3 and hence are interpreted as onlapping the lava flows.

There is a gradational passage upwards into a lithologically uniform, poorly bedded, coarse-grained tuffaceous sandstone that is composed mainly of plagioclase crystals and angular grains of lava, tuff and siltstone. The sandstone is well-jointed, and characteristically rusty weathered along joint surfaces. It is exposed upstream to the ford (SD 18169293). The overlying sandstone is weakly bedded and medium-grained with interbeds of siltstone and mudstone. Siltstone becomes dominant higher in the sequence and there is a gradational passage, over a few metres, into greenish grey, non-marine, epiclastic tuff; the boundary lies approximately 30m downstream from the confluence with the small tributary from Pike Side.

Leave the Gill on the west side and follow the minor road to Locality 5.

Locality 5 Ulpha Copper Mine (SD 18669237) The mineral vein, formerly worked for copper ore, can be seen in the side of the disused shaft excavated in bedded tuff. Small quartz veins follow the ENE trending cleavage that dips 55° to the NW. Hematised country rock and quartz gangue, with traces of chalcopyrite, arsenopyrite and pyrite are present on the spoil tip to the east of the shaft.

ITINERARY 14

Ulpha-Kiln Bank Cross

E. W. Johnson, British Geological Survey.

1:25,000 maps SD 19 and SD 29 or Outdoor Leisure Map 6
The aim of this half day excursion is to examine higher parts of the Borrowdale Volcanic Group preserved within the major volcanotectonic basin centred near Ulpha, in the south-west Lake District. Volcanic and sedimentological features of a sequence of andesite and ignimbrite with interbedded epiclastic tuff are illustrated. The rocks have a penetrative ENE-trending cleavage. Stickle Pike provides a fine viewpoint for the southern Lake District and Morecambe Bay.

The itinerary involves 3km of walking and 300m of ascent, mostly over rough, bracken covered fellside. The geology and localities are given in Figure 35. Cars may be parked by the roadside to the south of Ulpha Bridge (SD 197929) where the excursion commences. If a second vehicle is available this could be left at Kiln Bank Cross (SD 215932) to avoid a further 3 km walk returning to Ulpha Bridge at the end of the itinerary (Figure 35).

Locality 1 Ulpha Bridge (SD 196929). Small crags of porphyritic, acid andesite with scattered xenoliths protrude through the alluvial terrace of the River Duddon to the west of the road. The massive, blocky-jointed nature of the exposures indicates that it is the central part of the lava flow that is exposed. In hand-specimen abundant plagioclase and scattered mafic phenocrysts are readily discernible. Andesite forms the rugged ground on the east side of the valley. It can be examined in more detail between Brantstocks (SD 199927) and Yew Pike (SD 203926) where the flow-brecciated top of the youngest lava crops out and from which the view north along the Duddon Valley towards Harter Fell can be appreciated.

Follow either the track via Birks, or the footpath alongside the river and through Birks Wood, to Locality 2.

Locality 2 New Close (SD 202932). The contact between the top of the andesite lava and overlying bedded tuff is exposed immediately east of Birks Wood. Follow the forestry boundary wall south-east for 120m. Interstices within the irregular, blocky, flow-brecciated top of the lava are filled with laminated tuff. Laminae are generally concordant with bedding in the overlying tuff, which is laminated to thin-bedded and strongly cleaved. Material in the spoil tip from an old slate quarry clearly shows the relationship between bedding and cleavage. Sedimentary features include microfaults and syndepositional folds probably caused by seismic activity during deposition of this water-laid tuff. Flagstone was probably worked from a now partly flooded opencut driven south-east into the hillside.

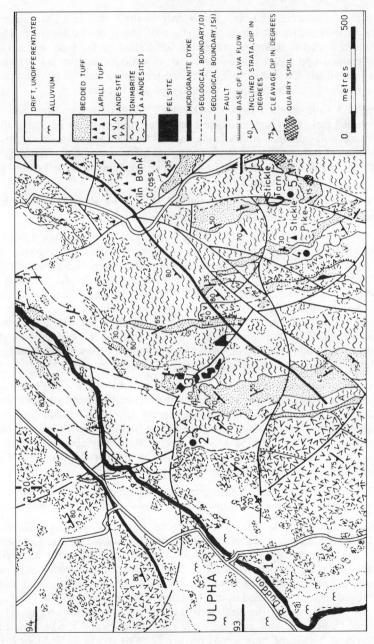

Figure 35. Geological map of the Ulpha area, Dunnerdale.

In the small crags 30-50m south-east of the opencut a heterolithic ignimbrite rests on an irregular surface of the thin-bedded tuff. The ignimbrite contains abundant and varied lithic clasts at the base, but in the finer grained upper part fiamme and a weak eutaxitic texture are present. Thin-bedded and laminated tuffs overlie the ignimbrite and can be examined to the south-east of the enclosure walls, on the way to Locality 3.

Locality 3 Hollow Moss Beck (SD 205932). Small trials for slate made in the bedded tuff 100m west-southwest of where Hollow Moss Beck and the enclosure wall intersect. Immediately east of the slate workings are several exposures of buff-weathered felsite, with many quartz veinlets. The felsite intrusion, a steeply inclined sheet or dyke, is cleaved and probably belongs to the Borrowdale volcanic episode.

Follow the stream south across faulted ground, to where it crosses the 250m contour (SD 20869260) near Locality 4.

Locality 4 Stickle Pike (SD 20979259 to 21199275). The south-west shoulder of Stickle Pike provides a typical section through a sequence of three units of rhyodacitic ignimbrite with tuff interbeds (Lickle Rhyolites of Mitchell, 1956, and possibly to be correlated with the lower part of the Airy's Bridge Formation). At the base, 100m due east of Hollow Moss Beck the upper part of the lowest ignimbrite is exposed. It contains non-vesiculated, essential lapilli and has a good eutaxitic texture. It is overlain by thin, parallel-bedded and laminated tuff. Reverse grading of lapilli in the coarse-grained bed indicates an airfall origin. A thin felsite sheet, lithologically similar to that seen at Locality 3, has been intruded subparallel to bedding near the base of the tuff.

A blocky-jointed, porphyritic acid andesite and rhyodacitic ignimbrite succeed this bedded tuff. The middle ignimbrite contains abundant lapilli and locally, near the base, is a rheomorphic breccia formed by slumping of the hot, but brittle material soon after deposition had ceased. The top of the ignimbrite is poorly defined and there is a gradational passage upwards over a few metres into bedded tuff. The thin and medium, parallel-bedded tuff is cleaved and a small quarry marks old workings for slate or flagstone.

The upper, rhyodacitic ignimbrite forms the summit of Stickle Pike. This has a weak eutaxitic texture, and contains abundant non-vesiculated, essential lapilli.

Stickle Pike provides panoramic views of the south-west Lake District; the Duddon Valley and Harter Fell to the north, Seathwaite and Coniston Fells to the north-east. North-northwest trending faults with westerly downthrow repeat the outcrop of the Lickle Ignimbrite ("Lickle rhyolite") on the side of Dunnerdale Beck and the lower slopes of Caw. To the south-east the rugged scenery produced by the BVG ends abruptly at the Lickle Valley which coincides with the sub-Coniston Limestone unconformity. The younger Ordovician and Silurian strata form prominent NE-SW trending strike ridges between Broughton Mills (SD 223906) and Bracelet Moor (SD 244919). Follow the path north-east from the summit to Locality 5.

Locality 5 Stickle Tarn (SD 21369281 to 21239314). To the west side of Stickle Tarn, the upper ignimbrite seen at Locality 4 is overlain by bedded tuff (Caw Tuffs of Mitchell, 1956). Here the boundary is gradational. The ignimbrite is weakly bedded near the top and is succeeded by thick, poorly bedded lapilli tuff passing upwards into thin, parallel-bedded tuff. After crossing the path that leads from Stickle Pike, trace the boundary north to SD 21239314. Near the base the tuff consists mostly of thin and medium, parallel beds. Approximately 5m above the base several beds contain abundant accretionary lapilli up to 1cm in diameter. These were deposited subaerially. The grain size of the tuff coarsens and bedding becomes thicker and less distinctive higher in the succession. Clearly evident is the ENE-trending cleavage. On steep slopes cambering rotates the cleavage planes in a downhill direction, reducing the amount of dip and modifying the strike direction.

Join the path that leads east to Kiln Bank Cross (SD 215932) where the itinerary ends. If a return to Ulpha is necessary the well-defined track through Kiln Bank Parks is recommended.

ITINERARY 15

Coniston to Levers Water

D. Millward and B. Young, British Geological Survey

1:25,000 map SD29 or Outdoor Leisure Map 6

This whole day excursion to the picturesque Coppermines Valley combines a study of volcanic processes within the upper part of the Borrowdale Volcanic Group with an examination of the remains of what was one of Britain's most important copper mining areas. The entire excursion involves a walk of some 7km and a total climb of about 470m using, for the most part, well-marked tracks. It is very important to remember that this area is riddled with old mine workings —great care should be taken as many of these are extremely dangerous. On no account should any of the workings be entered. A geological sketch map, showing the localities, is given in Figure 36.

The walk begins in Coniston where there is ample space for parking on all but the busiest of summer days. From there take the Coppermines track, located between the Black Bull Public House and Co-op, cross the cattle grid after some 500m and begin the excursion at Locality 1.

Locality 1 Round How (SD 29859800). To the right of the track on Round How are exposures of pink-weathered eutaxitic ignimbrite (Yewdale Breccia Formation). This deposit contains abundant lithic clasts and forms the uppermost unit of the BVG in the south-west Lake District. A few metres uphill are columnar joints within the same deposit that indicate a high temperature origin for these rocks.

Locality 2 (SD 29439806). Continue along the track noting the old Miners' Bridge. The deeply incised Church Beck, downstream from the waterfall, marks a fault and, to the left (south-west side) of the falls, beneath the bridge, the cleft marks the entrance to a trail adit driven along the hematised faults. The ice-smoothed rocks to the right of the track are bedded tuffs. These are laminated, fine to coarse-grained, locally with normal grading, long-angle cross-stratification and small channels with rip-up clasts (Tilberthwaite Tuffs).

150m upstream from the Miners' Bridge a small waterfall in bedded tuff marks the first view point. From here the main features of Coppermines Valley may be appreciated; the Bonser Dressing Floors in the valley bottom near to the white YHA building, Paddy End works to the left along Levers Water Beck, and Bonser Mine to the right, up Red Dell Beck.

Locality 3 Bonser Mine (SD 289986). The extensive dumps at Bonser Mine provide an excellent opportunity to study the mineralogy of the Bonser Vein. The main copper mineral, and the only one worked here, was chalcopyrite, though rare traces of tennantite ($(Cu.Fe)12As_4S_{13}$) have been found. The main gangue, as in most of the Coniston veins, was broken wall-rock and white quartz. At Bonser, magnetite was common and became increasingly abundant with depth. Although good chalcopyrite values continued at these deeper levels the magnetite rendered the ore impossible to dress by the available gravity methods, and led to the closure of the mine. The Bonser dumps contain large amounts of magnetite and chalcopyrite veinstone accompanied, in some examples, by botryoidal chlorite and plates of the black, 'brittle mica', stilpnomelane. Other minerals in the Bonser Vein include arsenopyrite, pyrite, pyrrhotite and small amounts of bismuthinite (Bi_2S_3) and native bismuth. Veins carrying galena and sphalerite, and nickel and cobalt minerals were also cut: the first two minerals may be found near the old powder house (now a cottage) at the north-west end of the dumps. Note the scarcity of secondary copper minerals: most of the Bonser workings were well below the oxidation zone.

Large scale mining at Bonser ended in 1895 though limited attempts at reworking took place early this century.

From here take the small track to the east of the buildings and proceed up Red Dell Beck, noting, at the point where the track crosses the stream, the dry-stone archway entrance to Bonser Deep Level (SD 28969882).

Locality 4 (SD 28819892). The steep south-west sides of Red Dell Beck are cut in closely jointed, dark grey, locally amygdaloidal, porphyritic andesite sills,; two are peperitic and mapping shows that they are cross-cutting to other strata.

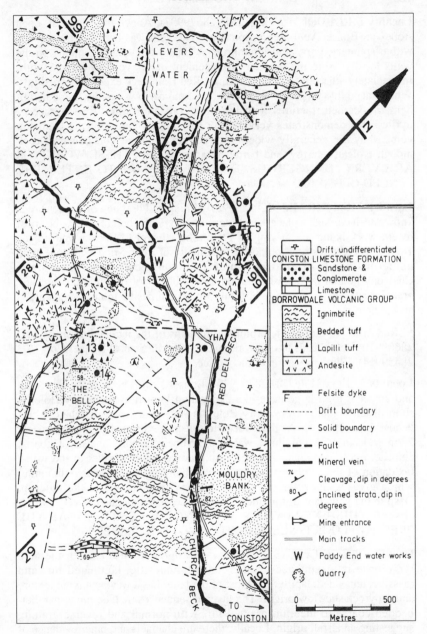

Figure 36. Geological map of the Borrowdale Volcanics and mineral veins of the Coniston area.

Locality 5 Red Dell Workings (SD 28679907). Above the waterfall, open stopes on Bonser Vein are conspicuous. The vein was here up to 1m wide within splintery, grey, acid ignimbrite. A little white quartz remains on the walls locally. Note the marked displacement of the vein by a cross fault. Immediately adjacent to these workings, Red Dell Beck exposes bedded tuff. When traced into this rock in the beck, the vein narrows rapidly into a belt of hematite-stained fractures with little mineralisation other than a trace of pyrite. This demonstrates very clearly a common feature of the Coniston veins: they are generally wide and productive in acid volcanic wall-rock though typically narrow and barren in andesitic tuff. THESE WORKINGS ARE VERY DANGEROUS. DO NOT ATTEMPT TO ENTER THE FENCED-OFF AREA.

Locality 6 Red Dell Mill (SD 286992). Mining and dressing of copper ore is known to have taken place here intermittently since before 1620, the most recent work being the driving of Flemming's Level to Bonser Vein in the 1820's. The dumps are composed principally of quartz-rich veinstone with numerous bands of chlorite which commonly coats quartz crystals. Chalcopyrite and pyrite are common. Small blades of bismuthinite and tiny granular aggregates of native bismuth can sometimes be found. Magnetite is absent here.

Return to the foot of the prominent remains of the inclined tramway (SD 28609910) which leads to old workings in Thriddle Scar of Kennel Crag (SD 28459914). Climb to the top of the incline.

Locality 7 Glory Hole (SD 28409917). Bonser Vein is here well-exposed in, and adjacent to, a large cave-like excavation known as the Glory Hole. A short distance south of the Glory Hole the vein is very narrow where it cuts bedded andesitic tuff. At the Glory Hole it has expanded to approximately 2.7m wide in acid ignimbrite wall-rock. Mineralisation consists of quartz, chlorite, pyrite and chalcopyrite forming crude bands parallel to the walls. Oxidation of the sulphides has produced abundant brown earthy 'limonite' which gives a characteristic rusty 'gossany' appearance to the outcrop. Despite the abundant iron oxides, oxidised copper minerals are very rare or absent. THIS EXCAVATION MUST NOT BE ENTERED AS THE PRESENT FLOOR IS SUSPENDED ON ROTTEN TIMBERS.

Locality 8 Erin Crag (SD 283995). Stratigraphically beneath the acid ignimbrite is a sequence of interbedded, andesitic, laminated tuff and massive, unbedded, lapilli tuff. Most of the latter has a weak eutaxitic texture and a pyroclastic flow origin. The layered sequences include much parallel-bedded coarse to medium-grained tuff with normal and reverse grading suggesting an airfall origin. Locally, there are channels and other evidence of reworking; some soft sediment slumping is also seen. Note the pink, porphyritic, rhyodacite dyke.

Descend the crags to the shores of Levers Water. The rocks exposed in the area of the dam are the acid ignimbrites seen at Thriddle Copper Mines. Note the numerous open stopes hereabouts (SD 280990) on a series of sub-parallel veins associated with Paddy End Vein. This vein has been extracted leaving the huge cleft, known as Simon's Nick, adjacent to Levers Water Waterfall. Some of these workings are very ancient and all are EXTREMELY DANGEROUS AND ON NO ACCOUNT SHOULD BE ENTERED.

Return to the well-marked track that descends the higher slopes of Levers Water Beck and about 200m from the Lake descend to the Beck.

Locality 9 (SD 28189904). The waterfall is in pink to white-weathered acid ignimbrite; note the splintery nature and the local eutaxitic texture. In the crags above the scree are stoped-outworkings along the Paddy End Veins. To the west of the tips the base of the crags marks bedded tuff separating two major ignimbrite sheets.

Locality 10 Paddy End Mine(SD 28359971). Cross the dumps from the Upper Level of Paddy End Mine to the head of the Paddy End Incline and follow this to its foot. Good examples of minerals representative of Paddy End Vein are abundant in the large dumps. Quartz and broken wall-rock, together with a little calcite and dolomite, are the main gangue. Chalcopyrite is the main copper mineral though tennantite is relatively common here. Pyrite is abundant and small specimens of bismuthinite and native bismuth may sometimes be found. Nickel and cobalt ores were found in small quantity. The bright pink cobalt secondary mineral erythrite ($Co_3(AsO_4)2.8H_2O$) is common on the Paddy End dumps together with examples of the hydrated copper carbonate and sulphate minerals malachite ($Cu_2 CO_3(OH)_2$) and langite ($Cu_4SO_4(OH)6H_2O$).

Locality 11 Quarry (SD 28409837). Near the water works at the site of Paddy End Works a small bridge crosses Levers Water Beck; follow this to the small quarry. In the lower part is strongly cleaved, thin-bedded to laminated, grey to green, medium to fine-grained tuff (Tilberthwaite Tuff Formation). Some beds are dark grey. Convolute lamination, ball and pillows and other forms of soft sediment deformation structures are indicative of subaqueous deposition. This sequence crops out over many kilometres from Broughton Moor, Walna Scar and the Old Man of Coniston through to Hodge Close and Little Langdale. It has been quarried for ornamental slate for several centuries. Evidence of this is vividly seen on the slope of the Old Man above this locality.

Locality 12 (SD 28379821). Climb uphill for about 170m and join the main track to Low Water. Beside the track is dark grey porphyritic andesite: mapping indicates this to be a sill, but note that it is uncleaved compared with the tuffs seen in Locality 11. Cleavage throughout the Coniston area is generally strong, but in places the more coherent rock types escaped severe deformation.

Follow the main track south keeping left at the junctions which are encountered within a few metres of each other (SD 28459810) and return to Miners' Bridge and Coniston via this path. If time permits two localities can be visited on The Bell.

Locality 13 (SD 286981). This dacitic lapilli tuff is strongly cleaved and it is commonly very difficult to identify rocks in this state.

Locality 14 (SD 287980). Coarse tuff, here generally parallel-bedded, but with some slumps, overlain by a very coarse, lithic-rich, dacitic ignimbrite.

Useful accounts of the history and archaeology of mining in the Coniston area have been given by Shaw (1970) and Holland (1981). The mineralisation of Bonser Vein has been described in detail by Stanley and Vaughan (1982).

ITINERARY 16

Nab Gill Mine, Eskdale

B. Young, British Geological Survey

1:25,000 map NY10 or Outdoor Leisure Map 6

This excursion demonstrates textural variation within the Eskdale Granite together with hematite mineralisation in fault veins in the intrusion. Good viewpoints from which to appreciate the broad geological structure of Eskdale are included. The total walking distance is a little over 2km with a climb of about 180m. Much of the route is along well-defined paths with a little scrambling over steep slopes in places. There are several old shafts and open stopes on the top of the fell and a few level entrances are still open. Extreme care should be exercised in the neighbourhood of these and on no account should any attempt be made to enter old workings. Between 2 and $2^1/2$ hours should be allowed. The geology and localities are given in Figure 37.

Cars may be parked at Dalegarth Station (NY 17300071). Walk to Boot village across the alluvial floor of the Esk Valley. Cross the bridge at Eskdale Corn Mill and continue straight ahead through the field gate to the east of Mill Cottage. Turn left immediately and proceed to the ruined buildings at the site of the former Boot Station.

Locality 1 Boot Station (NY 17550119). Outcrops of typical coarse-grained Eskdale Granite may be examined adjacent to the ruined buildings of Nab Gill Mine. A few metres south-west of these are the remains of the self-acting tramway built to carry iron ore from the higher levels of the mine to the loading bays at the end of the Ravenglass and Eskdale Railway. This railway, the predecessor of the present narrow gauge railway (known locally as 'La'al Ratty') was opened in 1875 to carry ore from Nab Gill to the main line at Ravenglass. The main period of mining at Nab Gill was between 1871 and 1884.

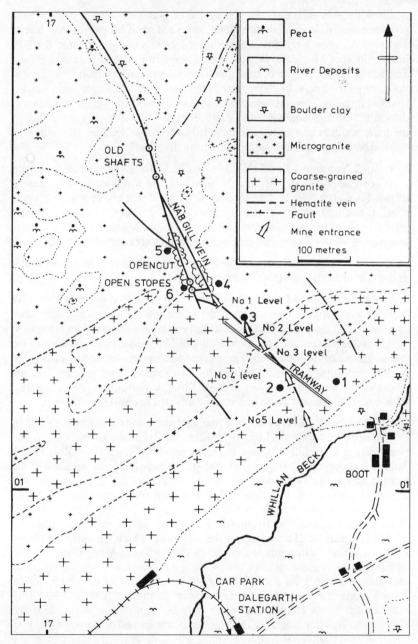

Figure 37. The Nab Gill mine area, Eskdale.

From the foot of the incline the course of Nab Gill Vein is marked by a prominent gully on the fellside together with red spoil heaps from the levels. The vein occupies a normal fault within the granite and can be traced NNW into the head of Mitredale. Branch veins diverge from the main vein in places. The filling consists of brecciated granitic wall-rock and hematite, much of it the kidney ore variety. In common with almost all other hematite veins in west Cumbria, gangue minerals are few, and comprise mainly quartz, calcite and dolomite. Nab Gill Vein varied in width from less than 1m to over 6m though the latter width is known to have included a 'horse' of granite. The mine was worked both opencast and underground from five levels.

Locality 2 Number 4 Level (NY 17470122). Outcrops of microgranite with scattered quartz phenocrysts may be seen adjacent to the collapsed entrance to this level. Irregular and commonly ill-defined patches of coarse-grained granite occur within the microgranite here, a feature common in the intrusion. Further uphill, where a short track branches to the west are other outcrops of microgranite with feldspar and quartz phenocrysts.

Continue up the incline past the dump from Number 3 level to the flat grassy top of the dumps from Number 2 level.

Locality 3 Number 2 Level (NY 17380133). The faulted nature of Nab Gill Vein is clearly apparent here in the sides of the gully which marks its course. Porphyritic microgranite forms the east wall and coarse-grained granite the west wall. Several narrow branches from Nab Gill Vein remain well-exposed in the coarse granite of the west wall. These consist of slightly-brecciated kidney ore forming bands parallel to the vein walls. The mammillated surfaces face the centre of the vein, clearly showing that filling was from the walls inwards. **Please do not hammer these outcrops or attempt to collect from them.**

The Number 2 Level dump is a fine vantage point from which to survey the main scenic and geological features of Eskdale. To the east is the prominent granite hill of Great Barrow capped by hornfelsed Borrowdale Volcanic Group lavas. Beyond this the pale-weathered joint surfaces of the granite above the Woolpack Inn and Youth Hostel are conspicuous. The distant horizon of Borrowdale Volcanic Group rocks includes the col on Hardknott Pass below which the straight, fault-guided Hardknott Gill descends into Eskdale at Brotherilkeld. To the south-east of this rises the distinctive peak of Harter Fell on the slopes of which, in certain lighting conditions, fine featuring in the volcanics may be seen. Along the south side of Eskdale the sombre cliffs of Gate Crag are composed of hornfelsed basalt and andesite overlying the Eskdale Granite, the contact of which can be traced along the foot of the crags. A row of dumps from old hematite workings at South Cumberland Mine may be seen on the lower slopes of Gate Crag. This line of crags is brought to an abrupt end at Hartley Crag by a group of parallel NNE-trending faults which displace the contact of the

Eskdale Granite southwards to Devoke Water. The view down Eskdale includes the long granite ridge of Muncaster Fell flanked on the south by the Esk and on the north by the Mite. Both valleys appear to be controlled by major east-northeast fault lines.

Above the Number 2 Level the incline is now in a very poor condition. It is therefore easier to proceed uphill to the site of Number 1 Level along the steep and narrow footpath.

Locality 4 Number 1 Level (NY 17310142). For much of its course between Number 2 and Number 1 Levels Nab Gill Vein proved to be barren with the vein filling composed mainly of hematite-stained granite breccia. A good exposure of this breccia, up to 3m wide, may be seen a few metres north-northwest of the partly collapsed entrance to Number 1 Level. Contemporary plans and sections of the workings indicate that payable hematite mineralisation was present a short distance NNW of this and the greatest tonnage of ore was won from the higher part of the mine.

Locality 5 old opencut (NY 17250148). Follow the gully on to the fell-top and cross the bracken-covered ground to the old opencut. A southern branch of Nab Gill Vein was worked opencast here. Remnants of the vein may be examined in the extreme southern corner of the pit where intensely brecciated ore, consisting of fragments of broken kidney ore (pencil ore) in a fine-grained matrix of crushed hematite, is exposed in contact with microgranite wall-rock.

From this point the course of the vein across the fell-top is marked by several old shafts. The dump from these (NY 17280149) has yielded, in addition to kidney ore, small samples of the black manganese oxide mineral romanechite.

Locality 6 old stopes (NY 17260141). The branch vein, here up to 1m wide and hading steeply to the east is well-exposed in the unworked portions of these stopes. The mineralisation consists of bands of kidney ore parallel to the vein walls.

From this, the highest point of the excursion, there are good distant views north-east to the Borrowdale Volcanic peaks of Sca Fell, Bow Fell and Crinkle Crags with, in the middle distance, the prominent crags of Eskdale Fell and Great How composed of hornfelsed volcanic rocks overlying the Eskdale Granite.

From the old stopes climb down the steep scree slope to the side of Number 1 Level. Good, small specimens of typical kidney ore may be collected from this slope.

From Number 1 Level the route is retraced to Boot village and the car park.

An interesting history of Ravenglass and Eskdale, including the associated history of iron mining in the dale has been given by Davies (1968). The geology and history of Nab Gill Mine has been outlined by Young (1984) and details of the geology of this and other mines in Eskdale have been published (Young, 1985a).

ITINERARY 17

Explosive volcanism and volcanotectonic subsidence at Crinkle Crags

M. J. Branney, Sheffield University

1:25,000 map NY 20 or Outdoor Leisure map 6

This excursion covers part of the Borrowdale Volcanic Group that shows typical evolution of a large basalt-rhyodacite ensialic arc volcano, in which early construction of basalt and andesite stratovolcanoes was followed by more acidic and much more violently explosive activity accompanied by major volcanotectonic subsidence, resulting in a caldera lake. The Borrowdale Volcanic Group (BVG) offers an unique opportunity to examine the internal form of a complex volcanic subsidence structure, as well as ancient subaerial lavas, and pyroclastics deposited by fall, surge and flow, including some controversial rheomorphic welded tuffs. For those unfamiliar with physical volcanology, the excellent general text by Cas and Wright (1987) is recommended. Detailed accounts of the volcanics of Crinkle Crags are given by Oliver (1961), Branney (1988a), and Branney and Soper (1988).

The excursion involves a full day's rough hill walking (9km) from Wrynose Pass over Crinkle Crags to Bowfell (Figure 38) and is best undertaken on a clear summer's day. Omission of the last locality can serve to shorten the trip considerably. There are no problems of access. Locality 1 is reached by foot in 1 1/4 hours by following the path from a car or mini-bus parked at the top of Wrynose Pass (NY 278026), via Red Tarn (NY 268037). Coaches should be left in Great Langdale, requiring a 2-hour walk in via Red Tarn. Localities are all given by grid references, and these may be plotted out on the 1:25,000 O.S. map NY 20 to advantage before embarking in the field. A hammer is not required, but a compass is strongly advised.

Locality 1 Ray Crag (NY 24360423). Leave the main path up Crinkle Crags just before reaching the first rocky summit (NY 252044), and cross country 800m west-southwest descending until you reach the top of Ray Crag, which offers excellent exposures of basalt lavas and tuffs of the Lingcove Formation (Branney, 1988b). The lavas include simple and compound flows in which both aa and pahoehoe morphologies can be recognised (Figure 39). The basalt weathers turquoise due to secondary amphibole, chlorite and epidote, and contains abundant walnut-sized amygdales. Thin units of bedded basaltic volcaniclastic rocks contain some fallout tuff, but show reworking into hollows and crevices in the lavas, probably by wind and ephemeral surface water. The entire 250m of basalt thins rapidly eastwards to pinch out completely within 3km. Above the basalts lies a 150m-thick andesite sheet with marginal breccias. One can debate whether it is a high-level sill (cf. Locality 7) or an extrusive block-lava. From Ray Crag there is an excellent view to the west, where the flat-lying Permo-Carboniferous coastal plain contrasts with the upland glaciated BVG scenery, with its U-shaped valleys (eg. Mosedale) and steep-walled corries of the Scafell massif. Periglacial solifluction lobes (on Hard Knott), scree, hummocky moraine (around Lingcove Beck) and alluvial cones (eg. below Stonesty Gill) are all well-displayed. Now walk 250m due east to Locality 2, where the top of the andesite forms a small bench.

Locality 2 (NY 24650420). The top of the andesite sheet is brecciated, with interstitial, cross-laminated sediment. This relationship is common in the Lake District, and occurs both at the top of high-level sills and lavas (Branney and Suthren, 1988). Have the interstitial sediments been washed down from the top of a lava, or do they represent vestiges of a wet host intruded by brecciating andesite (cf. Kokelaar, 1982)? The irregular top of the breccia is overlain by bedded tuffs and lapilli tuffs of the Whorneyside Tuff Formation (Branney and Soper, 1988). The base of the formation is marked by thin pyroclastic surge deposits (with low-angle cross-stratification), ignimbrites, and possibly some fall deposits. These pass upwards into increasingly massive ignimbrites, known as the Whorneyside Lapilli Tuffs, on whose weathered surfaces prominent lithic lapilli and recessed fiamme are visible. The fiamme (after welded pumice) often show reverse grading, typical of pyroclastic flow deposits. Non-welded pumice has been altered and is consequently unrecognisable in the field as is typical of the BVG. The ignimbrites can be traced for many kilometres (at the time of writing, from Rosthwaite Fell in Borrowdale, to the Duddon Valley in the south). They mark a major change in the BVG from dominantly effusive products below, to those of violent large-volume explosive eruptions. Well over 15km^3 of andesitic magma was erupted, probably in a matter of hours, entirely inundating former low-relief volcanic edifices. Thickness variations of the Whorneyside Lapilli Tuff indicate that the buried relief did not exceed 100m (Branney, 1988a).

Locality 3 Stonesty Pike (NY 24870403). 300m ESE of the last locality is the rather unimpressive peak of Stonesty Pike. Its steep western slopes exhibit massive Whorneyside Bedded Tuff. Evidence for a subaerial fallout origin of the bedded tuff can be assessed. Pyroclastic fall units rich in large lithic lapilli occur in the lower part of the bedded tuff. A few metres higher, a vertical face overlooking a prominent bench displays a fascinating imbricate thrust stack (Figure 40c) picked out by a repeated pale marker bed, 15cm thick, which contains abundant tiny accretionary or 'armoured' lapilli. The style of deformation indicate that it originated before final lithification of the tuff: fine ash was brittle and cohesive, yet coarse ash was easily disaggregated. Above the main crag, small fluvial box-channels with slumped sides draped by further fall units occur near the top of the bedded tuff (Figure 40B). The presence of steep-sided channels, along with the lack of preferred normal grading, general lack of cross-lamination in sand-grade

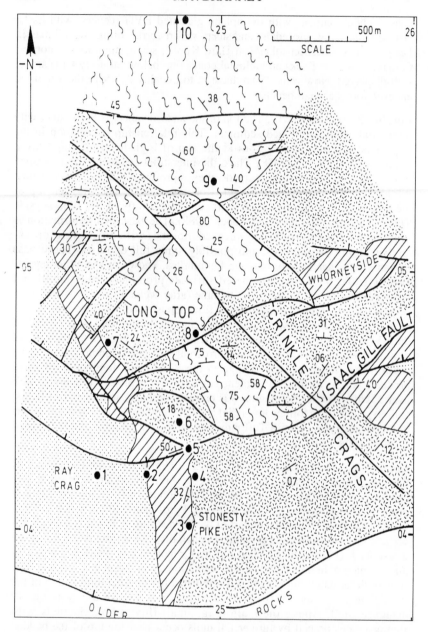

Figure 38a. Simplified geological map and stratigraphy of Crinkle Crags (after Branney 1998a).

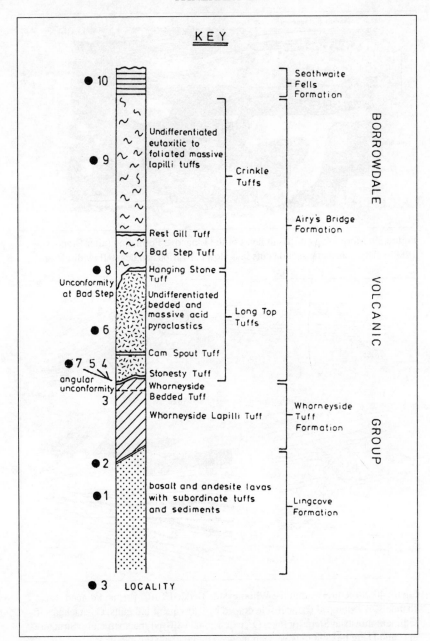

Figure 38b

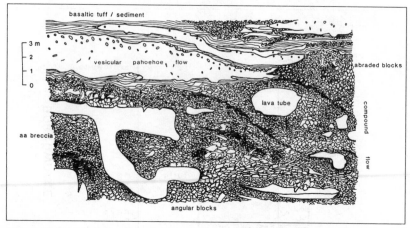

Figure 39. Morphology of basalt lavas of the Lingcove Formation (after Branney 1988b). This schematic section cuts lava flows at various angles to flow direction.

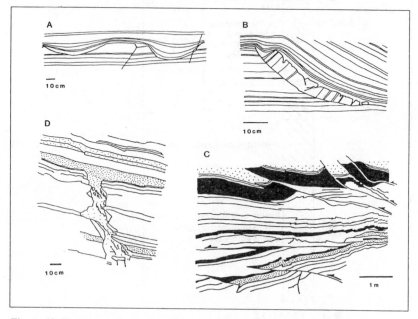

Figure 40. Structures within the Whorneyside Bedded Tuff. A - small draped channels, B - slumped channel side draped by subsequent fall units, C - stacked soft-sediment thrusts at Stonesty Pike, D - extensional soft-sediment structure. Structures in C and D are thought to have been induced by volcanic seismicity (after Branney 1988a).

beds, and the association (above and below) with thin beds of welded tuff, indicate subaerial deposition. This contrasts with a facies of the same unit at Sour Milk Gill (itinerary 21), where the ash clearly fell into ephemeral, shallow standing water. The Whorneyside Bedded Tuff is extensive, fine-grained, commonly crystal-rich, contains abundant accretionary lapilli, and exhibits random, parallel stratification (resulting from showers of damp ash). It is interpreted as a deposit from a phreatoplinian eruption. Such eruptions are the most violent known, and occur due to large-scale explosive interaction between water and magma, usually by eruption through a large lake or sea (Self and Sparks, 1978). The change from massive lapilli-tuff to bedded tuff emplacement occurred when access of water to the erupting magma increased eruption violence and lowered emplacement temperatures, partly by increased air-cooling. The abundant soft-sediment deformation structures, such as the thrust stack noted above, are widespread and were caused by seismic activity and block tilting whilst the volcano subsided following the rapid evacuation of andesitic magma.

Around the summit of Stonesty Pike, the pale-weathering, bedded basal unit of the Airy's Bridge Formation, the Stonesty Pike Tuff, can be seen resting unconformably on slumped Whorneyside Bedded Tuff. This unit is less than 2m thick, yet has been traced for over 20km around the Lake District.

Locality 4 (NY 24860420). Abundant soft-sediment deformation structures and rare lapilli impact-structures may be examined whilst following the crop of the Whorneyside Bedded Tuff northwards over gently sloping frost-shattered ground. The highly irregular, angular unconformity at the base of the pale-weathering Airy's Bridge Formation is excellently exposed. Immediately overlying the unconformity is the Stonesty Pike Tuff (Branney, 1988a) which includes surge deposits with accretionary lapilli, eutaxitic horizons, and beds which thin over palaeotopographic highs, occasionally pinching out completely. These pass up into acid eutaxitic pyroclastic flow deposits (ignimbrites).

Locality 5 (NY 2485031). A small E-W slack marks the position of a major volcanotectonic fault with a northerly downthrow. The far north side of the fault is marked by exposures of pale, acid welded ignimbrites of the Long Top Tuffs (Airy's Bridge Formation), but in the slack itself, some rather scrappy, flat exposures show Whorneyside Bedded Tuff slumped over the volcanotectonic fault. The bedded tuff normally dips gently south-east hereabouts, but immediately adjacent to the fault the tuff has suffered intense soft-sediment deformation, and dips steeply north down the fault plane. Exposures of acid eutaxitic tuff immediately north of the fault (best seen a few metres to the west) have steep, vertical, and random, welding-compaction fabric orientations, yet a couple of metres away from the fault dips soon become gentle and more consistent. Clearly, early faulting has

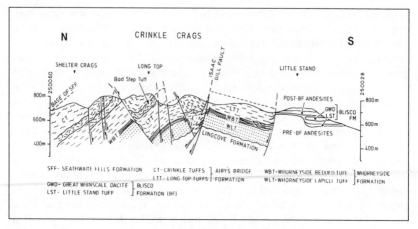

Fig. 41. True-scale section through Crinkle Crags, showing volcanotectonic faults and block-rotations (after Branney and Soper 1988).

affected welding-compaction fabric orientations. This, and similar faults in the BVG, separate blocks with different dips which were formerly interpreted as being due to a pre-Windermere Group compressional folding event (Soper and Moseley, 1978; Moseley & Millward, 1982), but many of the disparate dips are clearly due to penecontemporaneous rotations of fault blocks (Figure 40) involving extension and subsidence associated with successive volcanic eruptions. (Branney and Soper, 1988). If time is available, a visit requiring some 40 minutes can be made to Isaac Gill (NY 25820463) where this volcanotectonic fault is magnificently displayed in vertical section (Branney, 1988a).

Locality 6 (NY 24810442). A 40cm thick bedded tuff unit within the Airy's Bridge Formation, lying between two massive eutaxitic ignimbrite flow units, can be traced by a short scramble, traversing around the western side of the prominent crag just north-west of Locality 5. At the end of a narrow bench, half way up the crag, the bedded tuff unit is folded into a vertical isoclinal fold-pair, and adjacent eutaxitic fabrics show steep orientations. This is one of many linear zones of early deformation in Adam-a-Cove, where volcanic-related fault movements have variously folded or brecciated hot pyroclastic deposits prior to their initial cooling. Zones of intense deformation occur at least every 100m, reflecting a high density of underlying brittle faults, the geometry of which has not been entirely resolved. The degree of complexity can be ascertained by trying to trace any bed around the good exposures of Adam-a-Cove! The deformation is ascribed to several phases of subsidence and associated fault displacement accompanying the voluminous explosive eruption of the Airy's Bridge Formation pyroclastics. Scramble off the crag and walk 500m north-west, descending slightly, to Locality 7.

Locality 7 (NY 24440474). A long, low crag in the lower north end of Adam-a-Cove exhibits the top of a brecciated high-level andesite sill (described in Branney and Suthren, 1988) intruded into the Whorneyside Bedded Tuff just below the base of the Airy's Bridge Formation. The style of brecciation is identical to that of autobrecciated andesite lavas (cf. Localities 1 & 2), but it cross-cuts host stratigraphy 100m to the south-east, and its emplacement was fault-controlled, revealing its intrusive origin.

Above the andesite, the steep slopes below Long Top exhibit 180m of pale-weathering bedded and massive eutaxitic tuffs, the Long Top Tuffs (part of the Airy's Bridge Formation). Bedded eutaxitic tuffs are problematic, and may be ascribed to a number of primary emplacement mechanisms. Some 10cm thick beds show extremely low-angle truncations, and may have been formed by deposition from the base of thicker pyroclastic flows, although surge and fall deposits are also probably represented. The slopes from here to the summit of Crinkle Crags offer fine exposures of the lower part of the Airy's Bridge succession, to be compared with a greatly reduced succession on Base Brown, Borrowdale (itinerary 21). Massive pyroclastic flow deposits with crystal-rich bases and fiamme-rich tops can be recognised. These occur because heavier particles sink through pyroclastic flows whilst pumice, being more buoyant, tends to float. Ascend eastwards along the base of the steeper crags to meet the summit path at a cairned col on the main ridge.

Locality 8 (NY 24870481). Bad Step is a steep obstacle on the main ridge path encountered during the final ascent to the summit of Crinkle Crags. 20m west of it, an irregular-shaped acid dyke occurs at the base of the crag (Figure 42). It has flow-banded, almost aphyric margins gradational into a central coarse-grained porphyry, and it is cut by a smaller basic dyke. Such minor intrusions form the plumbing of the volcanic system. The acid dyke terminates upwards in a confusing brecciated mass.

About two-thirds of the way up the steep crag west of Bad Step a metre-thick bedded tuff forms a prominent bench, accessible from a little summit track to the west (Figure 42). It is a cross-bedded pyroclastic surge deposit, the Hanging Stone Tuff, which contains abundant multi-rimmed accretionary lapilli. It forms a valuable stratigraphic marker, having been traced for several kilometres around the Lake District to its type locality in Borrowdale (itinerary 21) where it is considerably thicker. It underlies a bedded pyroclastic breccia which contains angular blocks up to 1m across. The general absence of impact structures below the large clasts suggests that the breccia was emplaced laterally, by flow, rather than ballistically. Also, the

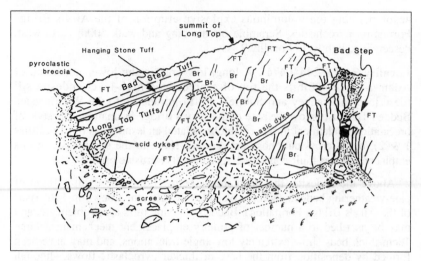

Figure 42. Sketch of Bad Step (locality 8) showing some stratigraphic and intrusive relations in the Airy's Bridge Formation. FT - foliated rheomorphic tuff, Br - breccia, acid intrusions - dashed (after Branney, 1988a). Note how the base of the Bad Step Tuff cuts down through the Hanging Stone Tuff and into the top of the Long Top Tuffs.

base is erosive, and cuts out the Hanging Stone Tuff towards Bad Step. The bedded breccia grades up into a highly welded, rheomorphic ignimbrite, the Bad Step Tuff. This is best examined around the summit cairns of Crinkle Crags. Any fiamme have been sheared out producing an almost continuous foliation. The tuff is high grade, which means that it was sufficiently hot on deposition to coalesce and flow like lava, producing the foliation, open folds, and an upper autobrecccia seen near the summit. Perhaps understandably, the Bad Step Tuff has been regarded as a flow-banded lava by some workers (Moseley and Millward, 1982), and as an intrusion by others (Oliver 1961); however recent mapping has revealed that its base is locally gradational into bedded accretionary-lapilli bearing tuffs and lithic lag breccias, whilst rare zones of discrete fiamme occur on Long Top.

The summit of Crinkle Crags is an excellent view point on a clear day, and one can get some idea of the size of the 'Borrowdale Volcano'. At the time of writing, the limits of the subsidence structure related to the eruption of the Airy's Bridge Formation are not yet defined, but work currently in progress indicates that it encloses the entire Scafell massif to the north-west, Bowfell, Glaramara and Rosthwaite Fell to the north, and Langdale Fell to the north-east. This entire area is characterised by intracaldera facies deposits (thick, high-grade, highly altered ignimbrites, with coarse, proximal breccias), dense volcanotectonic faulting, and is underlain by a shallow subvolcanic granitoid pluton (Branney and Soper, 1988). Erupted magmatic volumes of subsidence-related pyroclastics are in excess of 150 km^3. The subsidence structure is piecemeal and geometrically complex, with reactivation of structures during successive, overlapping subsidence events. The path northwards towards Shelter Crags (Locality 9) crosses more high-grade ignimbrites.

Locality 9 (NY 24980538). Volcanotectonic faults repeat the northward-dipping succession of Crinkle Tuffs (Airy's Bridge Formation) so that on Shelter Crags, the Bad Step Tuff is seen once again (NY 24980568). Here, another thinly-bedded marker unit, the Rest Gill Tuff infills and overlies the autobrecciated top of the Bad Step Tuff, forming a prominent feature (picked out by hachuring on the O.S. map). On the right-hand side of the path 50m north of this (NY 24670543), small-scale rheomorphic folds in Crinkle Tuffs are beautifully displayed on bleached surfaces by some peaty puddles. At NY 24860558, 15m west of the path, a eutaxitic lithic breccia occurs. Clasts of welded tuff are set in a welded tuff matrix. Is the breccia extrusive or intrusive?

Locality 10 (NY 2480 0630). The upper boundary of the Airy's Bridge Formation is faulted at Three Tarns. A path climbs northwards up Bowfell, across a magnificently exposed succession of lacustrine sediments and pyroclastics, known as the Seathwaite Fells Formation (Oliver, 1961). The sudden change to lacustrine conditions reflects major subsidence during the climactic eruption of the Crinkle Tuffs resulting in a caldera lake. Remember that immediately below the 200m of rapidly-emplaced Crinkle Tuffs, the facies are distinctly subaerial. Although some volcanotectonic faults are over stepped by the Seathwaite Fells Formation apparently without disturbance, the sediments exhibit spectacular evidence of continuing seismic activity (the abundant syn-depositional slump structures). Sediment supply rates were probably high and facies within the Seathwaite Fells Formation vary rapidly, strongly influenced by the continuing activity of some volcanotectonic faults. The extent of the lacustrine volcaniclastics has yet to be defined but is likely to have been subsidence-controlled.

The well marked route back to Wrynose Pass takes approximately 1½ hours. Alternatively, a quick descent to Great Langdale is possible via The Band.

ITINERARY 18

Subaerial pyroclastics of Side Pike, Langdale

M. J. Branney, Sheffield University

1:25,000 map NY 20 or Outdoor Leisure map 6.
This short excursion provides an opportunity, rare in Britain, to examine good exposures of subaerially-emplaced pyroclastic rocks, where the deposits of fall, surge and flow may be recognised and distinguished from reworked volcaniclastic sediments. The itinerary is suitable in poor weather, and can be completed in 2¹/₂ hours although ample exposure provides much interest for further consideration. All exposures are easily located, and within a few hundred metres of parking space near a cattle grid (NY 28950510) on the road from Great Langdale to Blea Tarn (Figure 43). Coaches should be left in Great Langdale, from where Locality 1 may be reached by a short walk. Hammering is unnecessary and spoils outcrops.

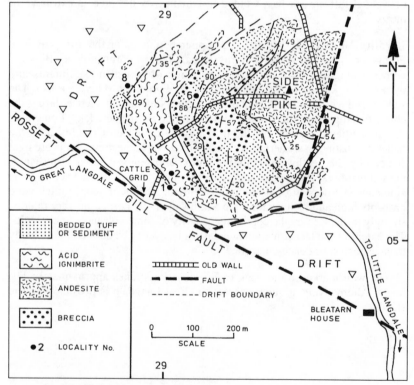

Figure 43. Map of Side Pike, Langdale.

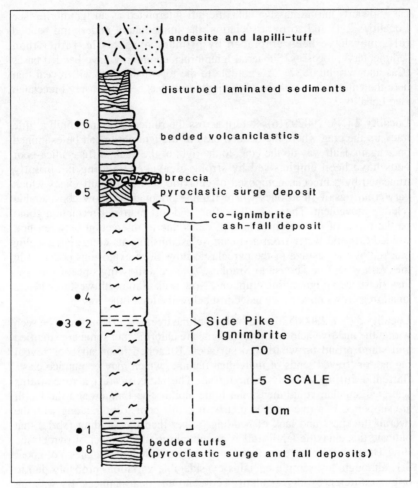

andesite and lapilli-tuff

disturbed laminated sediments

● 6   bedded volcaniclastics

●──── breccia
● 5   pyroclastic surge deposit

co-ignimbrite
ash-fall deposit

● 4

●3 ● 2   Side Pike
Ignimbrite

┌ 0

├ 5   SCALE

└ 10m

● 1
● 8   bedded tuffs
(pyroclastic surge and fall deposits)

Figure 44. Simplified log through some pyroclastics of Side Pike (after Branney, 1988a). Localities of itinerary 18 are indicated.

Locality 1 (NY 29000514). Cross the stile by the cattle grid, and turn right (east) across a ruined wall towards the prominent crag composed of 2m of brown-weathering bedded tuff (Figure 44). Low-angle cross-stratification occurs, and these beds could have been deposited by a combination of pyroclastic surge and fall (see Locality 8). The tuff passes up into 6m of pale-weathering silica-rich tuffs in which bedding becomes more diffuse and subtle upwards. A few beds contain fiamme, and at the south-east end of the crag careful examination will reveal low-angle bed truncations. These tuffs pass upwards into a massive eutaxitic tuff interpreted as an ignimbrite (see Localities 2-4) and so by association, the immediately underlying bedded tuffs may have been emplaced by primary pyroclastic, rather than sedimentary, processes. Subaerial ignimbrites commonly have bedded bases (Cas and Wright, 1987). A scramble to the top of the crag will reveal that here the entire upper portion of the ignimbrite has been intensely brecciated (see Locality 2).

Locality 2 (NY 29020516). Return across the ruined wall and climb a little track up the crag where the bedded base of the ignimbrite can be examined once again. Half way up the crag, to the right of the track, diffuse silica-poor beds have been emphasised by strong cleavage. Bedding is abruptly truncated by a breccia, composed of eutaxitic acid lapilli-tuff clasts which vary from jigsaw-fit to ones where fiamme orientations show considerable relative movement. There is a little fine acid tuff matrix. Brecciation could be the result of *in situ* phreatic explosions due to interaction between hot, welded tuff and water from a stream, re-establishing its course after being blocked by the passage of the pyroclastic flow. Such explosions occurred in the Valley of Ten Thousand Smokes, Alaska, following one of the few historic subaerial ignimbrite eruptions. Now walk 40m north-west to where a small tree grows on a grassy ledge just below the top of the crag.

Locality 3 (NY 29000520). At the base of the tree, large fiamme can be seen within the massive acid lapilli-tuff. Some are chloritic, but some are silicified and stand proud on weathered surfaces. Bleached joint surfaces reveal ragged, or 'frayed' ends of individual fiamme, which may be pumice clasts flattened during welding compaction. The eutaxitic tuff also contains scattered angular, equidimensional lithic lapilli. The fiamme and the lapilli are supported in a fine-grained matrix. It is this poor sorting, along with the overall thickness and lack of bedding (rather than the welding fabric) that indicate this eutaxitic lapilli-tuff is an ignimbrite, the product of pyroclastic flow. Here, fiamme have average flattening ratios (length/thickness) of about 8/1, although any sample contains considerable variation, probably due to original differences in vesicularity between individual pumices. By walking up through the ignimbrite, it can clearly be seen that average pumice flattening ratios increase towards the central part of the ignimbrite (Locality 4), and then decrease again towards the top. The ignimbrite thus represents a single cooling unit, which means that it was deposited quickly (though not necessarily from a single flow), and all cooled together. Varying size and abundance of fiamme are products of flow processes which occurred during emplacement, and may be used to define separate flow units.

Locality 4 (NY 29000528). Head northwards across a ruined wall on a peaty bench towards a lóne tree at the base of the next crag, noting that the fiamme become progressively more flattened upwards. At the base of the tree flattening ratios average 35/1, and fiamme can be seen deformed around small, equidimensional lithic lapilli. Detailed examination of the rest of the crag will reveal that average flattening ratios decrease upwards. This occurred due to cooling from the upper surface and because of decreasing load towards the top of the deposit.

Locality 5 (NY& 29030528). The top of the ignimbrite forms the obvious flat bench near the top of the crag. A brief search at the lip of this bench, 10-30cm below the grass, reveals a thin, fine-grained, cream coloured, porcellanous tuff. In places it contains abundant accretionary lapilli, about 1cm in diameter. It immediately overlies the top of the ignimbrite (which has flattening ratios of about 10/1). There is no sharp break or erosion surface here, and the fine, crystal-poor ash is probably a co-ignimbrite ash-fall deposit (Sparks and Walker, 1977), formed from vitric fines which escaped from the underlying pyroclastic flow during eruption. Such ash forms huge convective plumes which rise into the upper atmosphere resulting in extremely widespread distributions, a factor which should always be taken into consideration, for example, when sampling ignimbrites for chemical analysis.

Immediately overlying the co-ignimbrite ash-fall deposit, is 1-2m of cross-bedded, fine to coarse tuff, whose sorting and undulating sandwave bedforms suggest it is a pyroclastic surge deposit. The distinction between pyroclastic surge and fluviatile deposits can be problematic in ancient volcanics, but is here supported by the absence of diagnostic fluviatile facies sequences, and by a close association with the underlying ignimbrite: it must have been emplaced almost immediately after the ignimbrite, possibly during the same eruption, in order to protect the thin co-ignimbrite ash-fall deposit from rapid erosion. Cross-stratification typical of pyroclastic surge deposits can be examined by walking either way along the bench.

Overlying the surge deposit, and forming the top of the long crag, is a coarse breccia which contains large, angular pink clasts of eutaxitic lapilli-tuff very similar to the underlying ignimbrite. Clasts have no impact structures, and the breccia rests on a highly irregular erosional unconformity. It is difficult to say whether it was emplaced hot or cold, but one possible explanation is that it is a secondary mass-flow deposit which reworked debris from around a crater formed by the phreatic explosions indicated by the brecciation of underlying ignimbrite seen at Localities 1 and 2.

A massive lapilli-tuff, 2m thick, overlies the breccia on a grassy bench. Examine other exposures around the old loose stone wall. There are more eutaxitic lapilli-tuffs, bedded tuffs, and some andesitic sediments. The sediments, best seen south of the wall at the base of the next crag, are laminated and cross-laminated. with occasional ripples and abundant tiny scour surfaces overlain by silt-grade intraclasts. There is much evidence of soft-sediment deformation. Note the irregular base of the overlying coarse andesite breccia which forms most of the 10m-high crag. Is it a scour surface or slump scar?

Locality 6 (NY 29070537). Tracing exposures northwards from Locality 5, keeping below the steep slopes of andesite breccia to the east, there is an increase in the degree of soft-sediment disruption, with abundant penecontemporaneous faults, slide surfaces, and vertical and even overturned bedding. Two possible causes of the disruption are the emplacement of the overlying brecciated andesite sheet or volcanotectonic seismicity. Side Pike forms a small part of the Side Pike Complex (Branney, 1988a), a chaotic array of large blocks up to 0.5km across, all characterised by intense soft-sediment disruption. Some blocks have a recognisable internal stratigraphy, whilst others, such as that forming Side Pike, are exotic in that they have yet to be correlated with known Borrowdale Volcanic Group stratigraphy. There are many possible causes of such megabreccias, which are known to occur during caldera collapse or sector collapse of a volcanic edifice.

The adjacent eastward rise in ground is formed of a brecciated andesite sheet. Is it a lava flow, or an intrusion into wet volcaniclastics (Branney and Suthren, 1988)? It fails southwards after a few metres, where it passes into laterally variable, andesitic lapilli tuffs. This is typical of the complexity of subaerial volcanic sequences.

Locality 7 (NY 29380530). The entire stratigraphy at Side Pike is truncated by a volcanotectonic fault which forms the col separating Side Pike from Lingmoor Fell. 75m south of the col the contact is seen, and acid welded tuff with a steeply inclined eutaxitic fabric occurs as though plastered onto the surface of a steep andesite face. One can speculate on the origin of this interesting relationship. Across the fault, Lingmoor Fall is composed of acid ignimbrites, and volcaniclastic sediments intruded by andesite sheets. The fell offers excellent views of typical upland glaciated scenery; the corrie of Stickle Tarn perched above the U-shaped valley of Great Langdale to the north, and the hummocky moraine around Blea Tarn to the west. A wooded gully by Blea Tarn House (NY 296047) is due to the Rossett Gill Fault which runs down Mickleden and through the col south-west of Side Pike. In the Borrowdale Volcanic Group, many of the faults which form such prominent features are post-BVG shatter-zones of only small displacement. In contrast, many important volcanotectonic faults of large displacement commonly have little, if any, present topographic expression.

Locality 8 (NY 28820540). If time allows on the way back to the car, the west slopes of Side Pike allow re-examination of the bedded tuffs seen earlier below the ignimbrite at Locality 1. They exhibit characteristics which suggest emplacements by pyroclastic surge with some pyroclastic fall. They have low-angle cross-stratification, pinching and swelling of beds, and contain abundant multi-rimmed accretionary lapilli over 1cm in diameter.

ITINERARY 19

The Tilberthwaite Tuffs from Langdale to Tilberthwaite

F. Moseley, Birmingham University

Outdoor Leisure Map 6, or 1:25,000 maps NY 20, NY 30.
The Tilberthwaite Tuff Formation, resting unconformably on underlying rocks, is one of the most widespread units of the Borrowdale volcanics. It extends from south-west of Coniston (the Broughton Moor and Walna Scar Quarries) through to Langdale and the Langdale Pikes, where I believe the Seathwaite Fells Tuff (Oliver, 1961) to be the same formation. Figure 45 shows that the outcrops of the Tilberthwaite and Seathwaite Fells tuff, on opposite sides of the Great Langdale Valley, are only 2 kilometres apart and that both directly overlie the Airy's Bridge Formation. The proximity and similarity of these sequences leaves little doubt in my mind that they should be correlated. Towards the east there are outcrops of similar tuffs at the same stratigraphical horizon on Loughrigg Fell, Rydal, and as far as Kirkstone (itinerary 1), but more work is necessary in these areas. The tuffs were first mapped by Hartley (1925 and 1932) as part of his "bedded tuff" unit and although the maps were of a reconnaissance nature they show the general

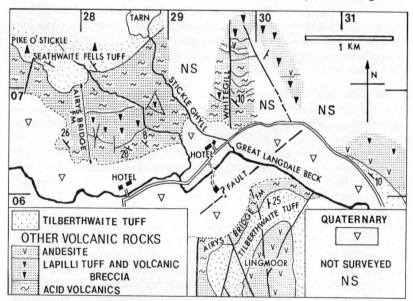

Figure 45. Sketch map of part of Great Langdale to show the supposed equivalence of the Seathwaite Fells Tuff and the (upper) Tilberthwaite Tuff. See figure 46 for continuation to the south.

distribution very well. Mitchell (1940) introduced the name Tilberthwaite Tuffs (lower and upper) for the outcrops in the Coniston region south of the ground covered by this itinerary. It seems likely that the lower Tilberthwaite tuffs represent an entirely different and earlier event from the upper division. They do not outcrop at Tilberthwaite, are separated from the upper division by ignimbrites and other volcanics, and I think that any future revision of the sequence should offer an alternative name, in which case the "Tilberthwaite Tuff Formation" would refer to the outcrops described here. I have also included Mitchell's (1940) Yewdale Tuffs within the Tilberthwaite Tuffs. Mitchell proposed the Yewdale Tuffs as a higher formation because there were andesites between them and the Tilberthwaite Tuffs, but it now seems likely that these are sills rather than lavas, and there is, therefore, no reason why all the fine grained ornamental (bedded) tuffs should not be regarded as the same formation.

This itinerary deals with the heavily quarried area of Tilberthwaite tuffs between Tilberthwaite and Great Langdale (Figure 46). Most of the quarries are now disused but preserve excellent, clean sections, perfect for examination of details, whilst some operate sporadically and may require permission to visit. The routes described are not physically arduous; the total walking distance from Chapel Stile, Langdale to Tilberthwaite and return is no more than 15km and can be covered in one day if desired, whilst there is little more than 400m of ascent. The itinerary can also be broken down into sections should one wish to spend longer on particular areas. A normal service bus runs into Langdale via Chapel Stile, but other roads are narrow and suitable only for cars and minibuses.

The Tilberthwaite Tuffs, like nearly all volcanic formations, vary in thickness and in details of the sequence, but the characteristic which has made them of great interest and economically important is their ornamental nature, shared with the Honister Tuffs. Together these formations form the "Green Slates" of the Lake District and are to be found as facing stones to buildings in most parts of Britain, and in many other countries. They also make excellent tables, lampstands, fireplaces, etc. The economically important parts of the sequence are volcaniclastic sediments, either deposited on the flanks of the volcanoes and reworked by fluviatile and lacustrine processes, or deposited directly into shallow lakes. There are now bedded alternations of fine to coarse material, with colours varying from pale and dark grey to pale and dark green. There is an infinite variety of sedimentary structure including horizontal, convolute and cross lamination, flute and load casts, flame structures, graded bedding, complex slumps and accretionary lapilli ("birds eyes", see glossary). The localities referred to below show many of these structures (see also itinerary 1). The economically desirable beds are up to 10m thick and alternate with unbedded coarse, medium and fine lapilli tuffs and with occasional andesite lavas and sills.

The whole itinerary can be covered in one day, although a number of exposures off the direct route would have to be left out. Alternatively it can be divided into smaller sections as indicated below. The advantage of the latter is that circular tours can be more easily planned, starting and finishing at the same place. These sections or tours are described A to C below.

TOUR A

Locality 1 (NY 316056). Take the road to Chapel Stile, Great Langdale. The abandoned Thrang Crag quarry exhibits good examples of the tuffs described above behind the row of houses now built in the quarry. Ascend Copthowe Gill at the NW end of the quarry where bedded tuffs in natural outcrop can be seen, followed by andesite, and then by medium to coarse grained lapilli tuff (about 100m of ascent is all that is required).

Locality 2 (NY 323051). The Elterwater quarries can be reached by crossing Great Langdale Beck on the footbridge near the hotel (NY 323052). The quarries are working again (1987) and permission to visit may be required. The same moderately dipping tuff horizons as those of Thrang Crag were well seen in a number of impressive caverns, although I have been told that renewed quarrying may have changed some of the outcrops.

Locality 3 (NY 316045). A minor surfaced road leads from Elterwater to Baysbrown and is joined by the footpath from Chapel Stile at NY 322046. Take the uphill quarry track to the abandoned Banks Quarry where gently dipping ornamental tuffs will be seen.

Locality 4 (NY 309042). Follow the path zig-zagging upwards to the Lingmoor ridge, above the top of Lingmoor quarries. Follow the wall and notice a number of bedded tuff outcrops. They are similar horizons to those of the Elterwater and Spout Crag quarries (Localities 2 and 9). Notice also the prominent escarpment which crosses the ridge by the bend in the wall (NY 307044). It is formed of amygdaloidal andesite, interbedded with the tuffs and is discussed under Locality 10.

Locality 5 (NY 306046). Just above the sharp bend in the wall the tuffs are followed by a porphyritic andesite with phenocrysts of feldspar and pyroxene (Hartley, 1932). This andesite forms a capping to the Lingmoor summit area and extends north as a rough "dip slope" to beyond Lingmoor Tarn and into Oakhowe Crag (Figure 46). The top is not seen.

Locality 6 (NY 298049 to 297049) Follow the footpath across the top of Lingmoor. At NY 298049 there is a sharp contact between the andesite and underlying gently dipping Tilberthwaite bedded tuffs. This outcrop needs investigating in more detail. Follow the path and the wall. At NY 297049, about 100m south-west of the wall the bedded tuffs are underlain by ignimbrite with good eutaxitic texture. It and other acid volcanics, which I

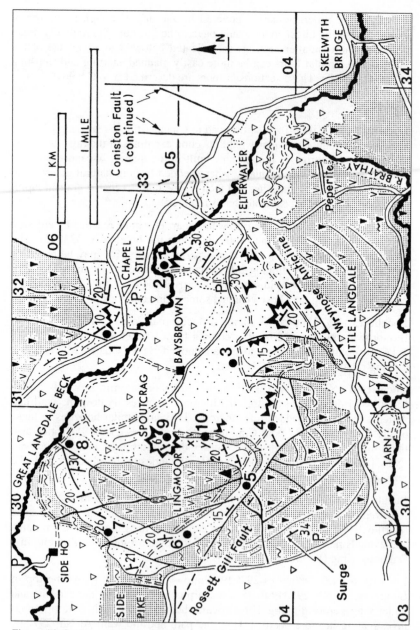

Figure 46. Outline map of the Tilberthwaite Tuff outcrop between Tilberthwaite and Langdale.

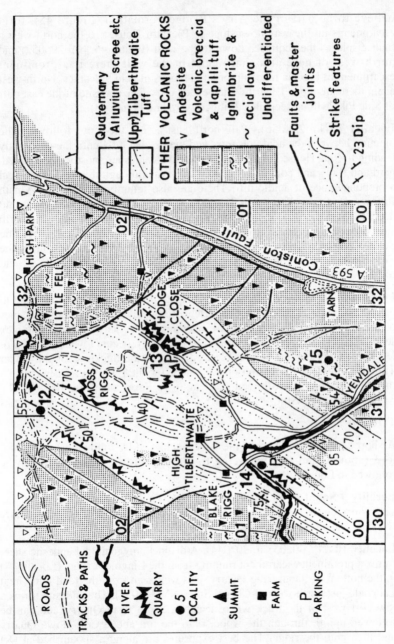

believe to be part of the Airy's Bridge Formation (Figure 45), form escarpments all the way downslope to Bleatarn House. To the north-west a fault displaces the sequence down to the west (Figure 46, NY 296052) and north-west of here at a sharp bend in the wall there is a prominent escarpment of breccia made up of large blocks of acid volcanics. North-west again there are more Tilberthwaite bedded tuffs. The andesite of the east cliff of Side Pike will be seen ahead (itinerary 18 and Figure 43).

Locality 7 (NY 298056). Walk north-east across the moor following the junction between the acid volcanics and the bedded tuffs until the deep gully leading to Side House is reached. The acid volcanics are mostly fine grained, hard and flinty and could be mistaken for lava, although thin sections reveal a preponderance of acidic tuff. There are also ignimbritic breccias. A path follows the top wall towards Locality 8. The view to the north-west and north takes in extensive outcrops of the Airy's Bridge Formation on the north side of Great Langdale, from Raven Crag to Whitegill (Figure 45). The Seathwaite Fells tuffs, which I believe to be the same formation as the Tilberthwaite tuffs, cap the Langdale Pikes (Moseley 1983, figures 62 and 67).

Locality 8 (NY 306060). Follow the footpath downhill alongside the wall to the northern end of Oakhowe Crag. Here, 30m above the path acid volcanics of the Airy's Bridge Formation are overlain by bedded tuffs with complex sedimentary structures. The andesite of Locality 6 occurs towards the top of Oakhowe Crag making it possible to determine the thickness of the Upper Tilberthwaite Tuff Formation on Lingmoor (about 150m). From Locality 8 the footpath can be followed via Oakhowe Farm and New Bridge (NY 317057) to Chapel Stile.

TOUR B

A short circuit from Chapel Stile is best achieved by following Localities 1 to 3 (above), and then retracing to the Baysbrown road which can be followed to Locality 9.

Locality 9 Spout Crag Quarry (NY 306051). This quarry has tuffs of the same horizon as the Elterwater and Thrang quarries, and is sporadically worked. The dip is 6° northeast.

Locality 10 (NY 306051 to 307044). A distinct amygdaloidal andesite sheet forms a prominent escarpment running from the Lingmoor ridge (Locality 4) to the bottom of Spout Crag Quarry. It is well seen from the road into Great Langdale just north-west of Chapel Stile (NY 315057). The andesite forms a low cliff west of the track where it enters Spout Crag Quarry, and can be followed uphill, through the wood, onto the fell above Colt Howe Quarry and then onto the ridge. The best exposures are along a stream bed at (X) (NY 307048), where there are water smoothed surfaces, and at the top of the scarp at (Y) (NY 307047), where the junction between the andesite and the overlying tuff is easily examined. The junction is irregular with fine grained tuff near the contact locally silicified to hornstone, whilst the andesite is brecciated with tuff filling the cracks. The andesite appears to be an intrusive sheet and is interpreted as a shallow peperitic sill (Branney and Suthren, 1988). Formerly this andesite sheet would have been regarded as a lava with a flow brecciated top.

Should one so wish, it is possible to follow the andesite escarpment to Locality 4 and rejoin the route of tour A. There is an awkward wall at NY 307047 just above (Y) but on the ridge a stile crosses another wall (at the bend, NY 307044).

To continue with tour B return from Y to X to Spout Crag Quarry and follow the track towards Baysbrown, turning left for Oakhowe and Locality 8 where the sequence described above can be seen. Return to Chapel Stile as indicated under Locality 8.

TOUR C

This represents that section of the itinerary from Little Langdale to Hodge Close and Tilberthwaite. From Tour A Little Langdale can be reached from the Lingmoor ridge (Locality 4) by following a path which descends to Dale End (NY 317038). Outcrops close to this path are of coarse to medium, unbedded tuffs below the main bedded horizons, but good bedding can be seen at NY 315042 and in the old Howe Banks quarry (NY 318041). Notice that all the localities so far described are characterised by gentle to moderate dips, mostly to the north-east, but south of Little Langdale the dip becomes steep, often vertical, with a north-easterly strike. The north-easterly trending Wrynose Anticline follows the Little Langdale valley.

Locality 11 (NY 313033). Take the footpath from High Birk Howe (NY 313032) near the Three Shires Inn. Notice the prominent rounded hills of till, on the eastern side of which there are bedded tuffs dipping 60° SE.

Locality 12 (NY312030). Follow the path to the Slaters Bridge and then to the abandoned and spectacular Little Langdale quarries (313028) where steeply dipping ornamental tuffs are well exposed.

From here there are several possible routes since the whole region between Little Langdale and Tilberthwaite is dotted with disused quarries some of which have been reopened. I recommend following the well defined track from the ford (NY 316029). Upon reaching the bottom of the Moss Rigg slate tip (NY 315023), a path diverges to the left (east). Follow it across the beck, and skirt old slate tips to the left (north). Good specimens can be obtained from this tip. The path leads on to Hodge Close quarry. Moss Rigg quarry (NY 312024), now working again, is also well worth a visit.

Locality 13 (NY 317017). I regard the disused Hodge Close quarries as the most impressive in this region, and possibly in the entire Lake District. There are two deep holes, the most southerly with deep water in the bottom, and the northern one accessible by a path which leads to a tunnel and to communication with the southern quarry. The beautifully bedded tuffs are vertical and strongly cleaved. They exhibit a great variety of sedimentary structures (Moseley, 1983). Should one wish to do the excursion in reverse order there is ample car parking at Hodge Close.

Locality 14 (NY 305009). Follow the road south-west from Hodge Close. Just beyond Holme Ground Farm at NY 309011 a signposted path leads to High Tilberthwaite. Tilberthwaite Gill follows an important NE trending shatter belt (Mitchell, 1940 and 1970) and parallel to it there is a series of quarries in steeply dipping tuffs. There are good parking facilities here also.

Locality 15 (NY 315005). I include the outcrops on Raven Crag merely in passing. Columnar jointed ignimbrite is well exposed and is part of the Yewdale Breccia Formation which is stratigraphically above the Tilberthwaite Tuff. It is a stiff climb from the road to the top of the crag.

An alternative to the climb from Yewdale to Raven Crag is to follow the path from the southern end of Hodge Close Quarry (NY 316015). It is a most attractive walk through oakwood and past the Welcome Nook slate quarry, until, just short of the second gate (NY 313012), there is an angular turn uphill. In 5 minutes along this path the northern extension of the Raven Crag ridge (Holme Fell) will be seen. The high points from NY 315006 to 314005 are formed of the eutaxitic and columnar ignimbrite.

ITINERARY 20

THE LOWER BORROWDALE VOLCANIC GROUP OF BROWN KNOTTS, BORROWDALE

Roger J. Suthren, Dept. of Geology, Oxford Polytechnic

Outdoor Leisure map 4, or 1:25,000 maps NY 21 and 22
This itinerary occupies a half day to a full day, depending on length of time spent on individual outcrops.

This excursion demonstrates the lower andesitic part of the Borrowdale Volcanic Group (BVG), which shows here a mainly subaerial pile of andesite block lava flows, with interbedded reworked volcaniclastic sediments, deposited in alluvial and lacustrine environments, and subordinate pyroclastics. The rocks to be examined belong to the Falcon Crag Formation and the lower part of the Thirlmere Andesites (Suthren, 1977).

Approach the area by the B5289 southwards from Keswick. Cars and minibuses may be left in the large National Trust car park at NY 272212, or in the small car park at the B5289/Watendlath road junction (NY 269203) or above Ashness Bridge (NY 270197). There is no parking for coaches: passengers could be dropped close to the Watendlath road junction, whilst the coach returns to Keswick to park. Car parks and localities are indicated on the accompanying map (Figure 47).

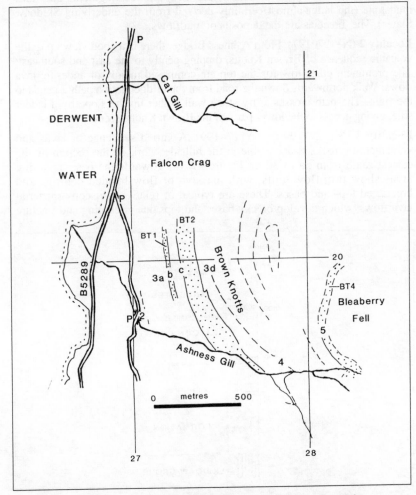

Figure 47. Geological sketch map of Brown Knotts area, Borrowdale. Major volcaniclastic units are stippled, most of the unshaded area consists of massive and autobrecciated andesite. P indicates car parks.

Locality 1 (NY 269209). The shore of Derwentwater, near the mouth of Cat Gill. The contact between the Skiddaw and Borrowdale Volcanic Groups is not exposed here, but is probably a steep, north-south trending fault, lying just offshore. The outcrops on the shore and in the road cuts are the lowest unit of the BVG exposed hereabouts, and consist of coarse volcanic breccias: the "Purple Breccias" of Marr (1916). The breccias are chaotic, unsorted and unbedded, with mainly angular clasts ranging in size from sand to boulders. Clast types include andesitic and acidic lava, pumice fragments and dark mudstone (the latter almost certainly derived from the underlying Skiddaw Slates). The breccias are the deposits of mudflows.

Locality 2 (NY 270197). From Ashness Bridge, there is a good view up to the volcanic sequence of Brown Knotts, dipping gently to the east and southeast. The prominent crags towards the top are composed mainly of andesitic lava flows. Walk northwards down the road from the bridge, until a path ascends to the right. The path crosses a dry stone wall higher up the slope by a ladder stile, giving access to the lower parts of the Brown Knotts section.

Locality 3 (NY 271199 to NY 274199). A varied sequence of lavas and volcaniclastic rocks is accessible in the hillside: work up the section by the easiest route from 3a to 3d on Figure 47. (a) Towards the base, andesitic lavas show thin flow units, with massive or flow-banded centres, and brecciated tops and bases, These are typical of relatively viscous subaerial lava flows, which develop blocky bases and tops due to cooling and fracture

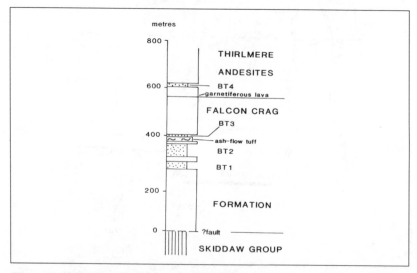

Figure 48. Generalised stratigraphy of the Borrowdale Volcanic Group in the Brown Knotts – Bleaberry Fell area. Major volcaniclastic units stippled, andesite lavas and sills unshaded.

whilst the hotter centre of the flow continues to move. (b) Above these, several tens of metres of reworked volcaniclastic rocks (BT1, Fig. 48) include conglomerates with well-rounded clasts up to 1m across, composed mainly of andesite, in a sand-grade matrix. In places, these are seen to be confined within steep sided channels, eroded into bedded volcaniclastic sandstones, Measurement of many pebble orientations suggests transport towards the north. The sandstone and finer conglomerates show parallel bedding and trough cross-bedding, and have silt to clay grade interbeds. Soft-sediment faulting is common. The erosional and depositional features are thought to be the result of transport and deposition by streams running across and dissecting the unconsolidated pyroclastic material of an andesitic volcanic plateau. Some of the parallel-bedded units may represent primary pyroclastic fall deposits. (c) The volcaniclastic unit just described is succeeded by a thick andesite flow, which disrupts the underlying sediments at its base. In turn, the andesite is overlain by reworked volcaniclastics (BT2, Fig. 48): a continuous low crag consists mainly of fine sand to clay grade sediments, which show laterally continuous beds with sharp, planar bases and tops. Beds are often normally graded, and show upward changes in sedimentary structures which resemble partial Bouma sequences. The vesicular appearance at the tops of some beds is due to the weathering out of small pumice fragments which, because of their low density, were deposited during the late stages of flow. The sequence is interpreted as the deposits of small, dilute turbidity currents in a shallow, temporary lake. It is abruptly overlain by coarser, cross-bedded sandstones deposited by stream flow (d) Continue up the section, which becomes steeper towards the top of Brown Knotts. A 10m thick massive lapilli tuff unit shows weak eutaxitic foliation and crude cleavage, and is the deposit of a hot pyroclastic flow. Its base is concealed by scree, but its top is sharply overlain by several metres of bedded and cross-bedded volcaniclastic sandstones (BT3, Fig. 48). Above this is a 20m thick andesite sheet, whose base disrupts the underlying sediments. The lower 2m of andesite are autobrecciated, whilst the centre of the unit is massive, with a characteristic blocky fracture. The upper 6m of the andesite is also brecciated, and overlain by a zone of disrupted bedded sediment containing andesite blocks. This shows typical peperite textures, and is interpreted as the result of emplacement of the andesite sheet as a high level intrusion into wet volcaniclastic sediments (a peperite is a breccia of irregularly shaped magmatic fragments in a disrupted sedimentary matrix, produced by interaction between magma and wet sediment). As in other parts of the BVG pile, it is clear that not all andesite magma reached the surface: many sheets previously interpreted as lava flows are in fact sills (Branney and Suthren, 1988). The summit of Brown Knotts is capped by more andesite. On a fine day, there are splendid views westwards and northwards to the smooth outlines of the fells composed of sedimentary rocks of the Skiddaw Group. Note the strong contrast between these and the rugged, irregular form of the volcanic hills of this area and further south. The modern delta at the head of Derwentwater shows typical features of a fluvial-dominated delta, including tree-lined levées, and mouth bars where the main distributary channels debouch into the lake. Now walk southeastwards to:

Locality 4 (NY 279194). Scattered exposures and boulders on the north side of Ashness Gill show a lava rich in primary igneous garnet. The lava is flow-jointed, and contains dark green inclusions of more basic material up to 10cm long.

Locality 5 (NY 281196). From the head of the northern fork of Ashness Gill (NY 279194) a low crag extends northwards to NY 281199. Here, the most spectacular exposures of subaerially reworked volcaniclastic sandstones and conglomerates are seen (BT4, Figure 48). PLEASE DO NOT HAMMER. Structures include channels and steep-sided gullies, cross-bedding and soft-sediment deformation, including loads and flames, and channel bank collapse structures. A 1m thick, laterally continuous massive bed has a fine-grained basal layer, with coarse clasts concentrated 20cm above its base. At the top, thin vertical sheets of clay-grade material represent dewatering structures: the unit is the deposit of a volcanic mudflow. The sequence represents subaerial erosion and redeposition of loose pyroclastic material on an andesitic volcano, by streams and mass-flow processes. Above this sequence, andesites outcrop sporadically up to the summit of Bleaberry Fell (NY 285195). Return to the car park, either by retracing the approach route, or via the footpath on the south side of Ashness Gill.

ITINERARY 21

THE BORROWDALE VOLCANIC GROUP AT SEATHWAITE, BORROWDALE

Roger J. Suthren, Dept. of Geology, Oxford Polytechnic, and Neil Davis, Dept. of Geology, University of Sheffield

Outdoor Leisure map 4 or 1:25,000 map NY 21
This itinerary occupies a half day to a full day, depending on length of time spent on individual outcrops.

This section illustrates correlatives of pyroclastic sequences described at Crinkle Crags (itinerary 17, Figure 38) to demonstrate how the volcaniclastic facies change laterally.

Approach Seathwaite from the minor road which branches southwest from the B5289 at the entrance to Seatoller village. Cars and minibuses may be parked on the roadside verges north of Seathwaite Farm (NY 235122); coaches must be left at Seatoller car park (NY 246137). The itinerary is shown on Figure 49. PLEASE AVOID HAMMERING THE OUTCROPS.

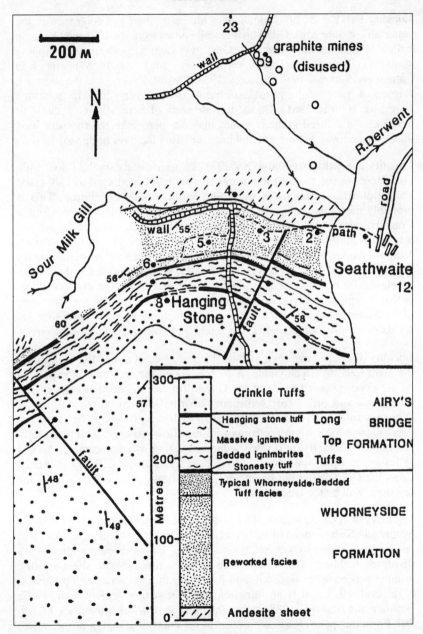

Figure 49. Geological map and succession north of Seathwaite, Borrowdale. Compare the succession with Fig. 38.

Locality 1 (NY 235129). From Seathwaite Farm, there is a good view of the waterfalls of Sour Milk Gill which cascade down from the U-shaped hanging valley of Gillercomb. Sour Milk Gill flows over a southeastward-dipping sequence of pyroclastic and sedimentary rocks of the Whorneyside Formation (Suthren, 1977; Branney, 1988a), whilst the crags to the south are formed of more acidic pyroclastic rocks of the overlying Airy's Bridge Formation (Oliver, 1961). On the hillside north of Sour Milk Gill, the spoil heaps of the disused graphite mines may be seen. Take the footpath west under the archway in the farm buildings, crossing the river bridge to:

Locality 2. Seathwaite Slabs (NY 233122), immediately south of Sour Milk Gill. Here we see the first exposures of parallel-bedded sand-to clay-grade volcaniclastic sediments of the upper Whorneyside Formation. This is probably the same unit as the Whorneyside Bedded Tuff seen on Crinkle Crags (itinerary 17, localities 3 and 4). Here. however, some of the ash fell into very shallow, probably temporary, lakes (Suthren, 1977; Branney, 1988a). Aqueous deposition is indicated by a variety of sedimentary structures including wave and current ripples, normally graded beds and rip-up clasts. Two coarser beds, showing single sets of tabular cross-bedding, probably represent fluvial deposition during flood events. On the south side of the Slabs, thick, massive breccia units, containing boulders more than 1m across in a poorly sorted matrix, are deposits of volcanic mudflows (lahars).

Locality 3. Ascend the steep path on the south side of Sour Milk Gill: this is the main route to Green Gable. A search around the path and on exposures on the opposite (north) side of the Gill will reveal desiccation cracks, sand volcanoes and other soft-sediment deformation structures within the Whorneyside Tuff. On the south side of the path, about halfway up, exposures exhibit a matrix-supported mudflow breccia, which strongly contorted the underlying bedded sediments during its emplacement. Ascend as far as the lip of the corrie, immediately south of the Gill (NY 228122). Cross the Gill (should not be attempted after heavy rain) and then cross the dry stone wall by the ladder stile.

Locality 4 (NY 228123). The southward facing outcrops of Upper Seathwaite Slabs consist of autobrecciated andesite, containing blocks up to 1m across, overlain by volcaniclastic siltstones and sandstones with strongly disrupted bedding. The relationship between the andesite sheet and the sediments is complex in detail, and it is likely that the andesite represents a high level sill, i.e. it is an intrusion into wet sediment (Kokelaar, 1982; Branney and Suthren, 1988) rather than a lava flow (cf. itineraries 17, 19, 20). From this point, look southwards to the crags of Hanging Stone, where breaks of slope pick out thick units of columnar-jointed ignimbrite within the pale-weathering Airy's Bridge Formation.

Locality 5 (NY 228122). Walk southwards from the last locality, recrossing Sour Milk Gill. We are now working up the sequence of the Whorneyside Formation. A variety of depositional and post-depositional structures is seen within the bedded lacustrine sediments and tuffs (Suthren, 1977). Certain horizons have been strongly affected by soft-sediment deformation. Soft-sediment deformation structures are abundant within upper parts of the Whorneyside Formation throughout the Lake District, and these have been ascribed to seismicity associated with the eruption of the voluminous Whorneyside Tuff (Branney, 1988a). Additional causes could be contemporaneous high-level intrusion of magma into wet sediment, or dewatering and slumping due to rapid, unstable accumulation of volcanic sediment. The upper part of the section, on the rising ground towards Hanging Stone, consists of thinly stratified parallel-bedded sand grade tuffs, typical of the Whorneyside Bedded Tuff facies described on Crinkle Crags (itinerary 17, localities 2 to 4). They were probably deposited subaerially by ash showers.

Locality 6. Walk southwest to NY 228121, close to the foot of the steep crags of Hanging Stone. We will now ascend the lower part of the pyroclastic succession of the Airy's Bridge Formation. The Stonesty Tuff is seen at the base of the Airy's Bridge Formation (Figure 49). It consists of up to 6m of thinly stratified accretionary lapilli tuff. The accretionary lapilli are ovoid objects up to 1cm long, often with a lighter coloured, fine-grained rim in a dark centre. The tuff exhibits bedforms typical of pyroclastic surge deposits (Cas and Wright, 1987), such as low angle cross-bedding, sandwaves with both stoss and lee sets preserved, and lapilli-impact structures. The accretionary lapilli formed by accumulation of concentric layers of fine ash around nuclei within a convecting steam-rich ash plume, or within the surge itself. The Stonesty Tuff has been traced for over 20km, from here to Dunnerdale, and is the basal unit of the Long Top Tuffs (the lowest part of the Airy's Bridge Formation) (Figure 49). Immediately overlying the Stonesty Tuffs are 30m of massive and bedded tuffs: they contain black fiamme which define a eutaxitic texture indicative of welding. One massive tuff unit, 8m thick, shows a well-defined lithic and crystal-rich base and an increase in concentration of fiamme towards the top. These features are typical of ignimbrites, the products of pyroclastic flows, in which denser components sink to the base of the flow, whilst low density pumice floats. Some thinly bedded eutaxitic tuffs also occur. These are difficult to interpret (Suthren and Furnes, 1980), and they could be combinations of flow, fall and surge deposits.

Locality 7 (NY 227120, 50m south of Locality 6). Overlying the bedded eutaxitic tuffs is a massive ignimbrite, 35m thick, which has a 2m thick crystal-rich surge deposit at its base. The lower 3m of the ignimbrite shows inverse grading towards a zone of blocks of welded tuff up to 2cm across.

The largest fiamme also occur within this zone. Passing upwards through the ignimbrite a gradual decrease in lithic fragments and crystals occurs. The top of the Long Top Tuffs is marked by a thinly bedded accretionary lapilli tuff, the Hanging Stone Tuff (Figure 49). This is the same unit as that figured at Bad Step in itinerary 17 (Figure 42). Around Seathwaite, the Long Top Tuffs are only one third of their thickness further south at Long Top (itinerary 17). Volcanotectonic collapse occurred concurrently with emplacement of the Long Top Tuffs, and this created a topographic depression to the south into which some of the ignimbrites ponded (Branney and Davis, work in progress).

Locality 8 (NY 228120, 100m southeast of Locality 7). The upper crags at Hanging Stone are composed of distinctive, massive, white-weathering tuffs, the Crinkle Tuffs (Figure 49). The Bad Step Tuff, which is the basal unit of the Crinkle Tuffs at Crinkle Crags (itinerary 17, Locality 8) is absent in this part of the Lake District. The Crinkle Tuffs exhibit excellent columnar cooling joints. Highly flattened fiamme are clearly displayed on bleached joint surfaces. The top of the Crinkle Tuffs is not visible from this locality, but they exceed 120m in thickness. In the Central Fells the Crinkle Tuffs show dramatic thickness variations (from 30 to 250m) across volcanotectonic structures related to collapse of a 'piecemeal' (i.e. intensely fractured) caldera (Branney and Davis research in progress). The Crinkle Tuffs were emplaced rapidly at high temperatures and they represent the culmination of a spectacular series of explosive eruptions. Before descending back to the floor of the corrie, observe the well-developed hummocky moraines in the floor of Gillercomb, and the excellent view of the corrie lip, hanging above the U-shaped Seathwaite Valley. Return to the vehicles by the path on the south side of Sour Milk Gill. Alternatively, recross Sour Milk Gill and proceed northwards to:

Locality 9 (NY 231128). The disused graphite mines. Graphite from Seathwaite formed the basis of the Keswick pencil industry (for further information, visit the museum near the Lakeland Pencils factory in Keswick). It occurs in irregular pipelike bodies associated with an altered basic intrusion (Postlethwaite, 1913; Firman, 1978), although its origin is enigmatic. Graphite may still be found on the spoil heaps which dot the steep hillside southeast from here. THE OLD MINE WORKINGS ARE UNSAFE. Return to Seathwaite using one of the numerous paths through the spoil heaps. A visit to the pencil museum in Keswick will be of interest.

ITINERARY 22

The upper Borrowdale Volcanics and lower Windermere Group S.W. of Coniston (Boo Tarn to High Pike Haw)

F. Moseley, Birmingham University

1:25,000 map SD29, or Outdoor Leisure map 6
This excursion examines one of the classical areas of the Lake District. Ash Gill Beck which is centrally placed gives its name to the Ashgill Series, and was described in detail by Marr (1916b) and subsequently by McNamara (1979). It is also one of the best areas to study the Caradoc unconformity between the Borrowdale Volcanic Group and the Coniston Limestone Formation, whilst the Ordovician-Silurian boundary is completely exposed with the Ordovician Ashgill Shale followed by the richly graptolitic Skelgill Shales of Llandovery age. Structurally the rocks dip steeply to the south-east and are displaced by several faults. A straightforward walk across open moorland allows the outcrop pattern of wrench faults and bedding thrusts to be appreciated as an important part of the Caledonian Orogeny.

The classical work of Marr, and easy access, have resulted in this area being visited by many individuals and excursion parties every year. There are numerous fossils throughout the sequence, but unfortunately there has been serious over-collecting, and visitors are asked to examine fossils in the outcrop and not to collect. There are extensive Windermere Group Collections in various museums, especially the Sedgwick Museum, Cambridge.

The Borrowdale Volcanic Group forms the lowest part of the sequence and commands much interest. In the north-east of Figure 50 the Coniston Limestone is underlain by the Yewdale Breccia Formation, mostly ignimbritic breccia with a streaky texture in the matrix, but in places more obviously ignimbrite with good eutaxitic texture. To the south-west, the Yewdale Breccia and the underlying formations of tuffs and andesites are progressively cut out where the Coniston Limestone oversteps the Ulpha syncline. This is the Caradoc unconformity, best studied around High Pike Haw (Figure 50).

The overlying Coniston Limestone Formation (Figure 4) is by no means all limestone, but includes conglomerate, sandstone, chert, mudstone, shale and some volcanogenic deposits. At the base there is conglomerate and sandstone, sometimes chertified; this is the Longsleddale Member (McNamara, 1979; Moseley, 1984) which is easily mistaken for Borrowdale volcanics since most of the fragments are volcanic derived. Occasional brachiopods and trilobites of Ashgill age (eg. *Encrinurus*) show that it is the basal member of the Coniston Limestone Formation (McNamara 1979). It is

F. MOSELEY

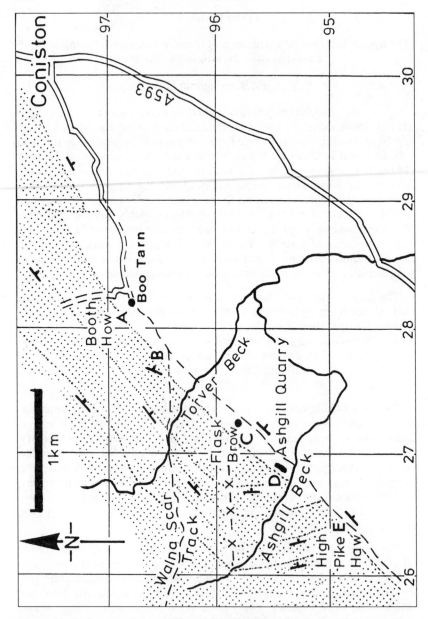

Figure 50. Outline map from Coniston to High Pike Haw. The Borrowdale volcanics are stippled, the Windermere Group is blank, the Ulpha syncline is indicated by X-X, A-D are map areas shown on figure 52, area E is referred to in the text.

followed by the Applethwaite Member, a strongly bedded nodular limestone with calcareous mudstone and thin volcaniclastic horizons. It has yielded abundant fossils including the trilobites *Calymene, Tretaspis* and *Phillipsinella*. The top of the Applethwaite member is gradational into the Torver member, a very fossiliferous mudstone containing *Phillipsinella* in particular. Marr (1916b) recorded 22 genera and species from these beds. The overlying white limestone is sparsely fossiliferous but McNamara (1979) has demonstrated a non-sequence between it and the underlying Torver mudstone. Another non-sequence is shown between the rhyolitic "ash" (Figure 51) and the Troutbeck-Ashgill Shale sequence. Troutbeck mudstones (Marr's *mucronatus* beds) were formerly highly fossiliferous (over-collected), whilst the Ashgill shales are less fossiliferous and dominated by brachiopods, although trilobites have been recorded. There is a strongly lithological contrast between the grey Ashgill and black Skelgill shales, which, for field mapping purposes, can be taken as the Ordovician-Silurian boundary.

By contrast to the Ashgill Shale, the Llandovery Skelgill shales represent a deep water facies; they contain pyrite and numerous graptolites, and have been divided into 10 graptolite zones (Hutt, 1974-1975; Rickards, 1978) with an average of 30 species per zone. Those same authors found the lowest graptolite zone, about 0.3m of mudstone with mixed shelly and graptolitic fauna, present in the west and south-west of the Lake District but missing in the east. The overlying (Middle and Upper Llandovery) Browgill beds are green mudstones with occasional black graptolitic bands, whilst the highest part of the sequence seen in this immediate area, the striped mudstones of the Brathay Flags, are of Wenlock age and are best seen in Banishead Quarry (SD 248 960). Other descriptions of this and higher parts of the sequence will be found in itineraries 23 and 24. The walking distance from Boo Tarn to High Pike Haw is 3 to 4km with very little climbing, whilst the general area is shown on Figure 50, with details of localities given on Figures 51 and 52.

Locality 1 (SD 283971). Cars can be parked at Boo Tarn (SD   282986), although the last 800m is a rather rough quarry road. For those who prefer to keep to tarmac, and have no objection to the extra walking, there is parking next to the fell gate at SD 289970. From Boo Tarn there is an excellent view to the north-east of Timley Knott (Moseley, 1983), where massive Borrowdale volcanic rocks are overlain by the well bedded Longsleddale and Applethwaite Members of the Coniston Limestone Formation (Figure 51). It is an easy 10 minutes walk from Boo Tarn to Timley Knott where the Applethwaite beds are particularly obvious with strong bedding and weathered-out concretions, but the underlying Longsleddale beds are less so since they are composed almost entirely of volcanic sands and silts derived from the Borrowdale volcanics, so that a first aquaintance may well suggest

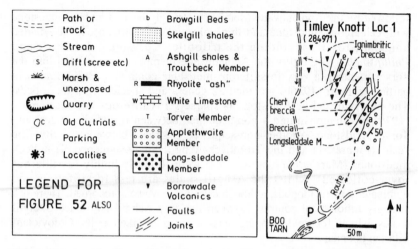

Figure 51. Legend for figures 51 and 52, and an outline map of Timley Knott, locality 1.

that they are part of the volcanics. However, the Longsleddale beds contain occasional Ashgillian marine fossils (see later localities and McNamara, 1979) which places them in the Coniston Limestone Formation. They are about 3m thick and partly silicified (chert).

Below the Longsleddale beds there are coarse bedded breccias with the same south-easterly dips, and below these are chert breccias, which have led to suggestions that all should be included in the Longsleddale Member, perhaps as local channel deposits. However, there are other considerations, for example a few metres uphill across low crags there is identical chert breccia dipping north-west, and a few metres further, chert breccia, now dipping south-east, is interbedded with ignimbritic breccia characteristic of the Yewdale Formation of the Borrowdale volcanics. I believe that the overall field relations leave no doubt that these breccias are truly part of the Borrowdale volcanics. The last outcrop is adjacent to the quarry road (Figure 51) from where it is a short walk to Locality 2.

Locality 2 (SD 28159690, Figure 52A). The Longsleddale Member will be seen forming a north-westerly facing feature. It is a sandstone made up of volcanic fragments and can easily be mistaken for the upper part of the Borrowdale volcanics.

Locality 3. 20m south-east of locality 2 there are exposures of the Applethwaite beds which immediately overly the Longsleddale beds.

Locality 4. 15-20m north-west of locality 2 extending further up the hill there are crags of the Yewdale Breccia Formation. It is polygenetic and frequently has ignimbritic streaks (eutaxitic texture) passing through the matrix.

Locality 5 (SD 28109680). Walk for 100m south of locality 4 across the head of a small gully and volcanogenic sandstone similar to that of locality 2 will be seen. It has lenticular interbeds of chert with occasional brachiopods, and is a part of the Longsleddale Member.

Locality 6 (SD 281967). Drop down the hill across fossiliferous Applethwaite beds to the Walna Scar "road". Just above the road at this point the first outcrop is a well defined slab clinging to the hillside. This is a dip slope of the White Limestone (Figures 51 and 52 A).

Locality 7 (SD 27879661). After 150m turn off the road along an ill-defined path which slants uphill: In 100m there is an outcrop of chertified Longsleddale beds with occasional weathered-out concretions (in a gully), and 50m beyond this, an excellent exposure of Applethwaite beds (Figure 52 B).

Locality 8 (SD 27819657). 70m south-west of Locality 7 enter a tributary of Summer Cove Beck. A variety of outcrops are to be seen within a 15m radius. The volcanic rocks in contact with the Longsleddale beds consist of eutaxitic ignimbrite underlain by volcanic breccia, and have a north-westerly dip compared with a south-easterly dip in the Longsleddale beds. The Longsleddale beds hereabouts (both sides of small faults) are medium grained volcanogenic sandstones, locally conglomeratic, and contain occasional brachiopods. The sandstone is overlain by Applethwaite beds (Figure 52 B).

Localities 9, 10, 11 (SD 277965). These localities are shown on Figure 52B. They are so close to each other that they are not described under separate grid references. Walk across the outcrop for 50 to 100m south-west of locality 8 where there are similar sequences. Notice a rib of Longsleddale sandstone with excellent fluviatile sedimentary structures at locality 9. At Locality 10 there is a 5cm thick conglomerate between the Longsleddale and Applethwaite beds, and at locality 11 there is ignimbritic breccia of the Yewdale Breccia Formation.

It will be noticed that localities 9-11 show near vertical dips to the ESE. The strike heads directly for the Skelgill and Browgill beds (Figure 52 B) which therefore truncate a large part of the Coniston limestone. The interpretation is not that of an unconformity, but of a strike fault along the Skelgill depression (see "structure" in the introduction).

Locality 12 (SD 278965). The small rib of cleaved mudstone adjacent to the footpath is part of the Torver Member (see McNamara, 1979).

164   F. MOSELEY

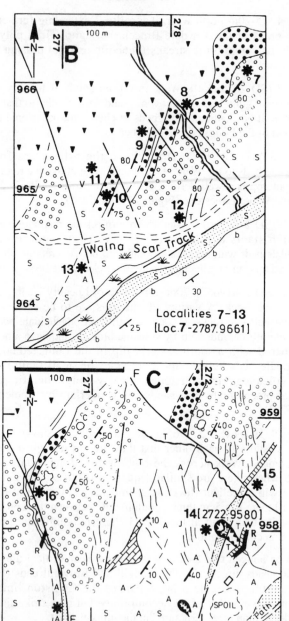

Figure 52. Maps showing the positions of localities 2 to 21, Boo Tarn to Ashgill.

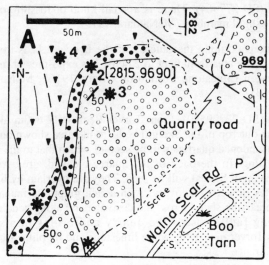

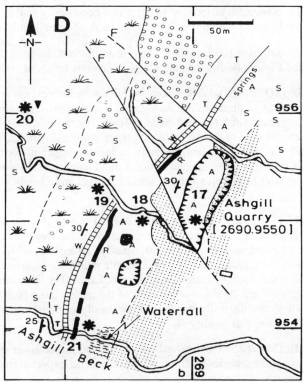

Locality 13 (SD 277964). There is a small knob of fossiliferous mudstone (Troutbeck-Ashgill member) (McNamara, 1979).

Follow the path along the outcrop of the Browgill beds to Torver Beck (SD 276962). The area from here to 274961 has exposures of most members of the Coniston Limestone Formation (Marr, 1916b; McNamara, 1979; Moseley, 1983).

Locality 14 (SD 27229580). From Torver Beck walk 600m along the path following the outcrop of the Skelgill beds, to the area shown on Figure 52C. Two small abandoned quarries will be seen of which that to the north-west is more interesting. In the back of the quarry cleaved, grey Ashgill shales (uppermost Ashgill Series) will be seen. They are overlain by black pyritous Skelgill shales (lower Llandovery) with a rich graptolite fauna (to find the graptolites break the slates across the cleavage and along bedding). A north-east trending fault crosses the quarry and brings in a sequence of fossiliferous Torver mudstone, white limestone and rhyolitic ash, the latter in the quarry entrance.

Locality 15. 60m north of locality 14 there is a good easily visible exposure of the White Limestone Member on the north bank of a small gully.

Walk up the gully for 100 to 150m. There is an obvious dip fault displacing the Coniston Limestone-Borrowdale volcanic junction by about 100m.

Locality 16 (SD 271959). Walk across the hillside to the next stream and the location of another prominent dip fault. Longsleddale sandstones are overlain by characteristic Applethwaite beds. I formerly thought that irregular hollows near the base of the Applethwaite outcrop were sink holes, but I now understand that they represent attempts to locate copper in former days. Follow this stream to the south and notice a small outcrop of rhyolite ash and also that the fault brings up a narrow strip of Ashgill and Skelgill shales (SD 271957).

Locality 17 (SD 26909550). Proceed to Ashgill quarry (Figure 52D). The quarry is of primary importance for its exposure of the Ordovician-Silurian boundary. The eastern face has recently (partly) collapsed and will require conservation. As with locality 14 grey Ashgill shales are followed abruptly by black Skelgill shales of completely different facies. The latter are pyritous and yield graptolites. At the southern end of the quarry a dip fault displaces the Skelgill shales dextrally by about 80m, easily established by walking along the beck towards locality 18.

Locality 18 (SD 26859550). Ashgill shales can be inspected in the stream and in inaccessible quarries to the south. These can be inspected from the top of the quarries.

Locality 19 (SD 26839553). On the south bank of the stream, immediately before the marshy area upstream, there are good exposures of the White Limestone and Rhyolitic "ash", which can be followed across open ground to Ashgill Beck. The lower part of the Coniston Limestone Formation is badly exposed hereabouts, and the White Limestone should not be mistaken for Applethwaite beds. It is easily distinguished by the sequence in this area.

Locality 20 (SD 268956). Walk 100m across the marsh to the first small knob of rock. It is eutaxitic ignimbrite belonging to the Yewdale Breccia Formation.

Locality 21 (SD 268954). Return to Ashgill Beck and the section described in detail by Marr (1916b), but notice that Marr's terminology has now been changed (McNamara, 1979; Moseley, 1984; and Figure 4). A full sequence from the Torver Member to the top of the Ashgill Shale can be studied.

Locality 22 (SD 264948). Follow the Skelgill shale depression to High Pike Haw (Figure 50E). Good sequences of the Coniston Limestone Formation are exposed hereabouts, and a little time spent exploring the adjacent volcanic rocks will reveal that they have easterly to ENE dips. Various volcanic formations are overstepped by the limestone revealing the nature of the unconformity.

The Windermere Group (late Ordovician and Silurian) of the eastern Lake District.

Two half-day itineraries, to Longsleddale and Kentmere, examine representative exposures of a 3000m sequence extending from the base of the Coniston Limestone Formation to the Bannisdale Slate Formation (Figure 53). The excursions may be taken separately, or, if transport is available at each end combined by walking the 4km from Longsleddale to Kentmere via the Stile End Pass making a total distance of 14km. The routes are, for the most part, along tracks or across low-level moorland. Some stream sections are included, particularly in the Longsleddale route. They can be dangerous when rivers are in spate.

The excursions are suitable as an introduction to the succession for those with some geological knowledge, but also include localities where the rocks can be studied in detail. A background to the geology is given in Lawrence, *et al.,* (1986), and in the Introduction.

ITINERARY 23

Longsleddale, Stockdale and Brow Gill (Coniston Limestone Formation to Brathay Flags Formation)

D.J.D. Lawrence and D. Millward, British Geological Survey

1:25,000 map NY 40 or Outdoor Leisure Map 7

This excursion of about 5km includes the classic localities of Stockdale Beck and Brow Gill, visits the type localities of the Longsleddale and Stile End Members of the late Ordovician Coniston Limestone Formation and examines the nature and field relationships of the Stockdale (Yarlside) Rhyolite (Figure 53).

NO HAMMERS SHOULD BE USED IN EITHER STOCKDALE BECK OR BROWGILL

A sketch map of the geology with localities to be visited is given in Figure 54.

Cars can be parked near the bridge at Sadgill (NY 48360568). Walk south along the road for 750m and turn left along the track to Stockdale. Continue past the cottages at the farm and descend to Stockdale Beck by the side of the Outdoor Pursuit Centre. The section upstream from here was described by Marr and Nicholson (1888) in their classic Stockdale Shales paper.

Locality 1 Stockdale Beck, old bridge to junction with Brow Gill (NY 49150539-49190555). Proceeding upstream a continuous succession is exposed from the Brathay Flags Formation to the Skelgill beds. The section

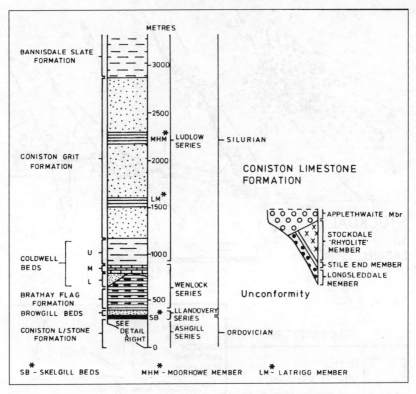

Figure 53. Generalised vertical section of the Windermere Group in the Longsleddale and Kentmere areas.

is illustrated in the inset Figure 54. Details of the rich Llandovery graptolite fauna can be found in the monograph by Hutt (1974-1975).

Grey silty-mudstone of the Brathay Flags Formation is exposed near the old bridge. The rocks show a fine, parallel lamination typical of the upper part of the formation, although exposed surfaces commonly represent cleavage rather than bedding. Graptolites of the *murchisoni* Zone can be found on the outcrops below the barn on the west bank: characteristic graptolites of this and lower zones in the Wenlock and Llandovery are illustrated in Lawrence *et al*; (1986).

4m upstream from the bridge a characteristic thin bed of tabular limestone nodules can be seen in both banks. Such a bed is present throughout the Lake District near the top of the *centrifugus* Zone.

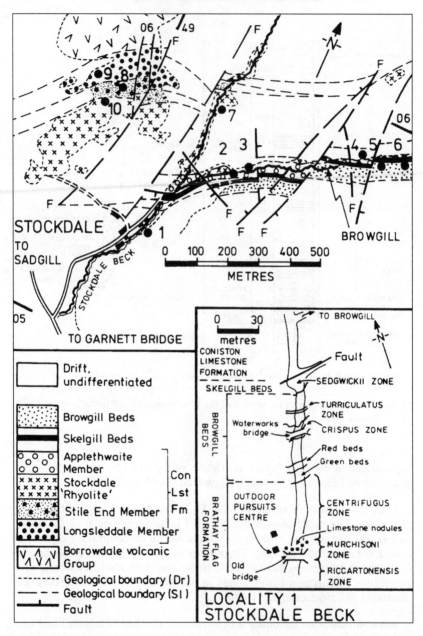

Figure 54. Geological map of Stockdale and Browgill, Longsleddale.

Further upstream the grey mudstone of the Brathay Flags Formation passes down into green mudstone of the Browgill beds. The base of the Brathay Flag Formation is taken at the stratigraphically lowest occurrence of dark grey, graptolite-bearing mudstone above the barren green mudstone of the Browgill beds. Pink and red mudstone with nodular limestone is well-developed in the upper part of the Browgill beds here, but it is uncommon further west in the Lake District.

Towards the base of the Browgill beds thin bands of black mudstone are interbedded with the green mudstone. These black bands yield the abundant graptolites which enabled Nicholson and Marr (1888) to subdivide the sequence. The highest of them can be seen immediately south of the Waterworks bridge (the Haweswater tunnel terminates in the hillside above the beck), where the Llandovery *crispus* Zone is represented by numerous black bands in strata beneath and just north of the bridge. About 6m of barren green mudstone separate the *crispus* zone from the 5cm thick black bands in 0.6m of pale grey mudstone which represent the *turriculatus* zone. The base of the Browgill beds is 2.5m below the grey mudstone. Black mudstone of the uppermost Skelgill beds can be examined up to a fault where a stream enters the east bank. Only the *sedgwickii* zone is present in the Skelgill beds here, faulted against the underlying Coniston Limestone Formation. A more complete succession within the Skelgill beds is seen in Brow Gill (Locality 4).

The upper part of the Coniston Limestone Formation is well exposed north of the fault at the southern end of the rapids in Stockdale Beck (NY 49190555). A few centimetres of dark grey, well-cleaved shaly mudstone of the Ashgill Shale Member overlies the interbedded mudstone and nodular limestone of the Applethwaite Member.

Continue north-east up Brow Gill. A sequence from the top of the Stockdale 'Rhyolite' to Browgill beds is exposed in a series of discontinuous strike-sections resulting from several NNE-SSW and NNW-SSE faults which cut across the stream.

Locality 2 Brow Gill (NY 49340566). About 200m from the junction with Stockdale Beck, the stream flows along interbedded limestone and calcareous mudstone from near the base of the Applethwaite Member. The limestone beds here are more continuous than those higher in the member.

Locality 3 Brow Gill (NY 49390569). The upper contact of the Stockdale Rhyolite is exposed 250m east of the junction with the Stockdale Beck. The intensely fractured and tuffaceous upper part of the 'Rhyolite' is overlain by conglomeratic basal beds of the Applethwaite Formation. The conglomerate, of well-rounded, subspherical rhyolite pebbles up to 1cm in diameter, is weakly bedded and contains thin intercalations of coarse-grained sandstone towards the base.

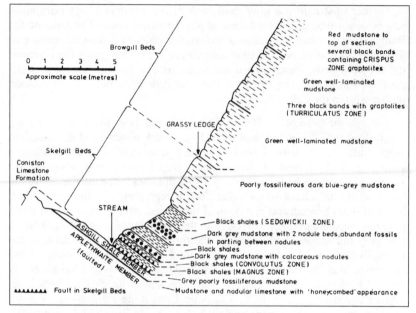

Figure 55. Sketch section of "The Rake", Browgill.

About 200m upstream from locality 3, a fault with easterly downthrow brings the Skelgill beds down to stream level. Ascending the gill the Coniston Limestone Formation forms a dip slope on the north-west bank and a steep scarp, composed of Llandovery strata, forms the south-east (left) bank.

Locality 4 Brow Gill (NY 49690584). The uppermost beds of the Coniston Limestone have, here, a characteristic 'honeycombed' appearance and pass into the grey, strongly bioturbated mudstone of Ashgill Shale, which has a maximum thickness of 1.2m in Browgill.

Locality 5 The Rake, Brow Gill (NY 49740587). A sequence from the Ashgill Shale up into the Browgill beds is exposed at this classic locality of Marr and Nicholson (1888). The main units to be seen are illustrated in Figure 55. On close examination the apparently massive black mudstone of the Skelgill beds is laminated, similar to the Brathay Flags Formation. Similarly, the apparently homogeneous grey-green and green mudstone of the Browgill beds is commonly laminated with silt and some discontinuous, streaky, blue laminae. Small pyrite cubes can often be found on fallen blocks of green mudstone. Thrust faults, sub-parallel to bedding, account for the absence of several graptolite zones near the base of the Skelgill beds at 'Rake'. Such faults are common within the formation throughout the Lake District.

Locality 6 Brow Gill (NY 49820591). High on the south-east bank of the stream, opposite the wall, the effect of the 'Stockdale Thrust' is displayed in a highly disturbed outcrop of Skelgill beds mudstone overlain by uniformly dipping, green mudstone of the Browgill beds.

Climb the hillside to the north keeping east of the wall. Pass through the gate, and descend west, across the boulder-strewn glacial drift to Stockdale Beck.

Locality 7 Stockdale Beck (NY 49210587). Low rounded knolls near the east bank of the stream are of pink-weathered Stockdale 'Rhyolite'. The strongly foliated felsite contains many flow-folds of variable style, orientation and intensity. In the beck, a few metres upstream, is hard, pale-grey, fine-grained sandstone (Stile End Member). The Stockdale 'Rhyolite' is exposed continuously downstream for about 300m.

Descend Stockdale Beck to join the tracks from Stockdale Farm. From the track pass through the gate (NY 49180557) and climb the hill to the north-west.

Locality 8 Old quarries (NY 48900574). These quarries expose the grey, fossiliferous, calcareous siltstone of the Stile End Member. Weathered slabs show good bioturbation structures and yield a varied fauna including trilobites, brachiopods and corals.

Locality 9 (NY 48820576). Farther up the hill the underlying Longsleddale Member consists of cyclic sequences of interbedded siltstone, sandstone and conglomerate. The conglomerate beds form prominent ridges with finer-grained sedimentary rocks between them. The conglomerates are poorly sorted and structureless. They contain sub-rounded to sub-angular pebbles and cobbles derived locally from the Borrowdale Volcanic Group including andesite, rhyolite, dacite, and lithic tuff. The sandstones form graded beds up to 0.5m thick and cross-bedding is found at several levels

Locality 10 (NY48870570). Descend the hill to a small quarry where the Stockdale 'Rhyolite' rests on cleaved silty mudstone of the Stile End Member. The base of the felsite is strongly sheared. A few metres south of the quarry the surface of the exposure has fine-scale 'onion-skin' weathering along perlitic cracking in the originally glassy rock. Nearby, in a south-facing crag there are football-sized nodules formed of aggregates of extremely large spherulites.

Continue south, downhill, observing the variably flow-banded and flow-folded, pink to grey felsite. Follow the track east to Stockdale and return to the bridge at Sadgill.

The excursion can be linked together by taking the track from Low Sadgill via Stile End (NY 467048) joining the route at Kentmere Church. The walk is 4km along an easy path with good exposures of the Stockdale 'Rhyolite' and Stile End Member.

ITINERARY 24

Kentmere

D.J.D. Lawrence, British Geological Survey

1:25,000 map NY40 or Outdoor Leisure map 7.

This excursion, of about 8km, examines Silurian rocks of the Windermere Group in a glacially modified landscape. The strata seen, from the Brathay Flags Formation to the Bannisdale Slate Formation (see Figure 56), consist of mudstone, siltstone and sandstone in varying proportions. Distinguishing between the formations requires careful observation of the rocks, both at outcrop and in hand specimen. It is recommended that a bottle of dilute hydrochloric acid should be carried to assist in identification of calcareous beds.

Cars can be parked near Kentmere Church (NY45630410). Ulthwaite Bridge (NY 45600118) provides a suitable place for transport to wait if itineraries 23 and 24 are being combined.

Follow the track towards Kentmere Hall. Looking west towards the Garburn Pass, the rugged crags of the Borrowdale Volcanic Group to the north contrast with the softer features of the sedimentary Silurian rocks to the south. A terminal moraine occupies the Kent valley between the track and the crags to the north. At the end of the last ice-age, shallow, ice-dammed lakes occupied part of the Kentmere valley with an upper lake north of the Force Jumb (NY 46040462) and a lower lake between the church and Millriggs (NY 457022). Parts of these lakes contain deposits of diatomite exceeding 15m in thickness. They are of post-glacial age and were worked for the manufacture of insulation products until a few years ago. The flat-bottomed valley to the south of Kentmere has resulted from the artificial draining of the lower basin in about 1840. Kentmere Hall, notable for its pele tower, is believed to date from the 14th century.

From Kentmere Hall take the westernmost track towards Whiteside End.

Locality 1 Parkbrow quarry (NY 45090379). The upper part of the Brathay Flags Formation was formerly worked here for roofing slate. Cleavage is almost coincident with bedding and produced flat slabs. However, the stone was generally found to deteriorate rapidly in use. In the quarry faces the rusty-weathered rock appears massive and well-bedded. It consists of finely laminated silty mudstone with partings and laminae of pale bluish grey siltstone, so that the rocks typically have a distinct parallel lamination at outcrop. The quarry has yielded graptolites indicating the Wenlockian *lundgreni* Zone.

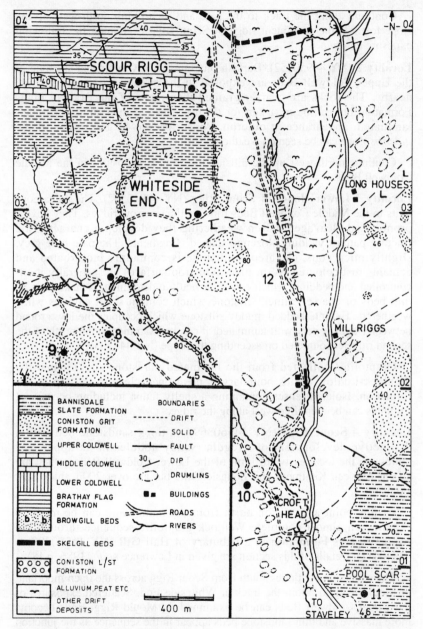

Figure 56. Geological map of the Kentmere area. L refers to the Latrigg Member of the Coniston Grit Formation).

Continue along the track to the gate and then climb north-west up the slope towards the prominent ridge of Scour Rigg examining the following exposure *en route*.

Locality 2 (NY 44950352). Darkish blue-grey, finely laminated siltstone of the Upper Coldwell Beds are exposed in the stream and on the hillside nearby. The rocks are coarser-grained than those of the Brathay Flags Formation but can be mistaken for them because of their similar, parallel-laminated, appearance at outcrop. Poorly preserved graptolites of the *ludensis* Zone can be seen on weathered surfaces.

Continue north-west up the hillside to examine exposures in the Middle Coldwell Beds.

Locality 3 Lower slopes of Scour Rigg (NY 49910362). The calcareous units in the Middle Coldwell Beds form distinct narrow ridges. They have a pronounced cleavage, and on weathering they develop a characteristic fracture pattern yielding 'lozenge-shaped' fragments. The pale blue-grey, slightly micaceous, calcareous siltstone is commonly bioturbated and contains rust-coloured worm tubes. Outcrop surfaces are generally joint-controlled and bedding, which can be difficult to determine, is picked out by thin beds of coarse-grained siltstone which contain small cavities when weathered. The interbedded muddy-siltstone which occupies the low ground between ridges is very well laminated; it can be examined to the north of the second ridge encountered on ascending the slope (NY 44850368).

Graptolites collected from the laminated mudstone suggest that the Wenlock-Ludlow Series boundary is positioned close to the top of the formation. Isolated lenses containing a shelly fauna including occasional trilobites can be identified west along the ridge.

Locality 4 Scour Rigg (NY 44560369). A thick sandstone bed with a distinctive development of irregular sandy nodules in its upper part represents the local eastward limit of the Lower Coldwell Beds, which are absent between Kentmere and Longsleddale, but are over 200m thick near Coniston.

At this point a diversion north from the main route can be made to examine an almost complete Wenlock graptolite sequence through the Brathay Flags Formation in a tributary of Hall Gill (NY 44550399 to 44710411). Details of this section are given in Lawrence *et al*, (1986, p.18).

The excursion continues south from Scour Rigg across the open moorland of Mould Rigg to rejoin the track at Whiteside End. Scattered exposures of the Upper Coldwell Beds can be examined on Mould Rigg. Beds become more massive and thin sandstone beds appear in the sequence as the junction with the Coniston Grit Formation is approached. The boundary is gradational and arbitrary.

Locality 5 Whiteside End (NY 44910294). Massive medium to coarse-grained sandstone in the lower part of the Coniston Grit Formation is seen north of the track. The beds appear homogeneous at outcrop and bedding direction is difficult to determine, unless the mudstone or siltstone top of a turbidite unit can be identified. Round or oval cavities up to 0.15m in length are sometimes developed parallel to bedding. The Coniston Grit Formation is dominantly turbidite sandstone divided by two lithostratigraphical units composed mainly of finer-grained beds, the Latrigg and Moorhowe Members (see Locality 7).

Follow the track westwards, largely over glacial drift.

Locality 6 (NY 44550292). Thinner bedded units in the Coniston Grit Formation can be examined in the stream north of the track. Some of the turbidites have a rippled mudstone top. The rocks generally dip steeply to the south, but local variations in dip can be recognised in the stream section. 110m north of the track an anticlinal closure trends WSW-ENE across the stream.

Continue along the track to the sheepfold (NY 44280274) then take a poorly defined path south-east across some large drift mounds, to join Park Beck.

Locality 7 (NY 44500255). In the south bank of the Beck, for 100m east towards the wall, finely laminated siltstone and fine-grained sandstone of the Latrigg Member is exposed. The beds are fine-grained turbidites, composed mainly of Brathay Flags type laminated muddy-siltstone and mudstone, but with some units having a basal sandstone with ripples and convolute lamination. The strata are relatively incompetent and have been affected by folding to a greater extent than the surrounding massive sandstone.

In Park Beck, for some 700m downstream, the turbidite sequence of the Latrigg Member and overlying Coniston Grit Formation is well-exposed and can be examined in detail. The rocks display a variety of sedimentary structures and faults; overturned beds and small folds can also seen.

Cross the beck and follow the path south towards Croft Head (NY 45450137). At the gate stay on the north side of the wall and walk west towards the sandstone outcrops.

Locality 8 (NY 444023). Comparison of dips within the sandstone exposures reveals gentle folding in the Coniston Grit Formation. N-S linear striations visible on the surface of some outcrops result from ice-scouring during the last glaciation.

Locality 9 (NY 44280220 and 44170218). Further west along the wall, several outcrops display sedimentary structures on bedding surfaces. Load structures and transverse ripples are particularly well seen.

Return to the gate (NY 44570237) and continue south-east along the track to Croft Head over hummocky glacial drift with large grit boulders scattered on the surface. The position of the Latrigg Member is marked by a slight north-east to south-west depression (NY 445019).

Locality 10 Path junction north of Croft Head (NY 45380145). Large drumlin mounds become common towards Croft Head, where the Kent Valley narrows.

The circular route, and return to Kentmere, follows the track north-east to Sawmill Cottage (NY 45420166), but a diversion can be made via Ullthwaite Bridge (NY 45600118) to examine the Bannisdale Slate Formation at Pool Scar.

Locality 11 Pool Scar (NY 45930081). The typical 'striped' or 'banded' facies of the Bannisdale Slate Formation can be seen in the crags, consisting of thin-bedded, bluish grey, fine-grained, micaceous sandstone, siltstone and mudstone. A close-spaced fracture cleavage is well-developed in the finer-grained lithologies. It is uncertain whether the adit at the west end of the scar yielded any mineral, although lead was worked around Millrigg Knott (NY 463015).

Locality 12 Kentmere Tarn (NY 455028). From Sawmill Cottage follow the track north past the works. The drainage of the old lake basin between Millriggs and Kentmere (see above), led to the discovery of a thick deposit of diatomaceous earth in the post-glacial lake sediments. Kentmere Tarn has resulted from the flooding of the old diatomite workings.

Return to Kentmere Hall by the path through Hall Wood, and rejoin cars at the church.

ITINERARY 25

The Westphalian and Permian Geology of the Whitehaven Area

N.S.Jones and P.D. Guion
Department of Geology, Oxford Polytechnic

1:25,000 maps NX 90/91 1:50 000 map 89

The purpose of this excursion is to examine Upper Carboniferous (Westphalian) and Permo-Triassic sedimentary rocks which are well exposed in cliffs and quarries around Whitehaven. The cliffs and quarries are easily accessible on foot but the wearing of walking boots and safety helmets is advised. As the different localities are widely spread (Figure 57), the use of a car or mini-bus is desirable. The geology of the area is covered by the B.G.S. 1: 50,000 sheet 28 (Whitehaven). We will be examining rocks of Westphalian B and C age and the unconformity with the overlying Permo-Triassic rocks (Figure 58).

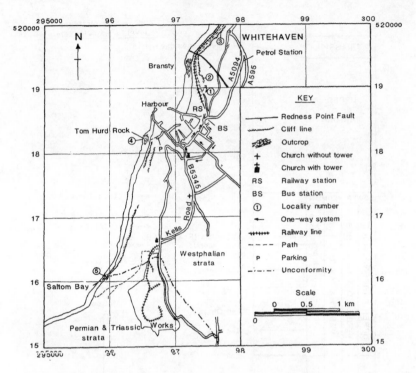

Figure 57. Map of the geological localities in the Whitehaven area.

Locality 1 Bransty Cliff (NX 97501880).

Access to Whitehaven is usually via the A66 and then the A595. As Whitehaven is approached, take the A5094 right hand turn which leads down a hill towards the town centre. At the bottom of the hill take the first turning on the right before reaching the bus station and immediately take a left turn off. This road becomes a track, and vehicles should be parked about 100m from the turn on an expanse of waste ground on the left. Walk about 20m following a path towards a cliff section about 15m high which is visible to the right of a warehouse.

The cliff section consists of sandstones which are Westphalian C in age and were formerly referred to as the "Whitehaven Sandstone Series". This sequence of rocks was once considered to have an unconformable relationship to underlying strata on the basis of its difference in colour and lithology. These cliff sections consist of fine to medium-grained red sandstones with prominent cross-bedding and ripple cross-lamination, produced by the migration of subaqueous dunes and ripples respectively. Halfway up the cliff a 3m thick set of tabular cross-bedding is present, with

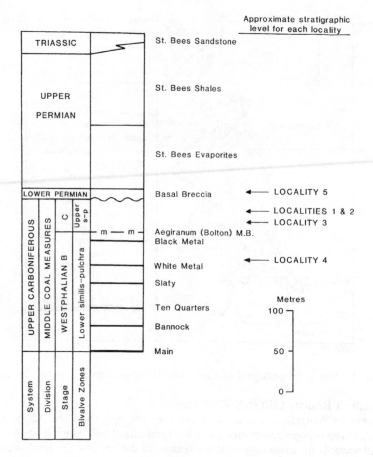

Figure 58. Generalised stratigraphic section for the Whitehaven area.

foresets representing the successive avalanche faces of a fairly straight-crested barform which migrated towards the southeast. The cross bedded sandstones at this locality are interpreted as the deposits of a large channel system.

Locality 2 Bransty Cliff (NX (97481904).
This locality can be reached by walking along the gravel track approximately 100m northwards from the last location. A 20m high quarry exposes the same sandstone body as that of Locality 1. The reddened sandstone, which is fine to medium-grained, has an erosional, rather unconformable, base which is exposed on the foreshore although this is not easily accessible. The sand

body can be sub-divided into three units separated by erosion surfaces with associated lag-conglomerates containing intraformational claystone and siltstone clasts. The mean palaeocurrent orientation differs for each of the 3 units, but palaeocurrents show a low variance within each unit. The dip of the major bedding surfaces is also different for each unit. Each of these 3 units may be termed a storey which represents the deposit of an individual fluvial palaeochannel, and the stacking of these units forms a multi-storey sequence.

The second unit from the base contains low angle(10°) bedding surfaces representing coset bounding surfaces which dip towards the right (southwest). Each coset is locally erosively-based, tapers downwards, and contains asymptotically-based planar to trough cross-beds up to 30cm thick which were formed by the downstream migration of subaqueous dunes. Palaeocurrents from these cross-beds are dominantly parallel to the dip direction of the coset bounding surfaces. The low-angle bounding surfaces are interpreted to represent the previous positions of the lee slope of an intermittently migrating large sandy barform. The similarity between cross-bedding and bounding-surface orientations suggests that the barform developed by the downstream accretion of subaqueous dunes within a channel on the gently dipping lee side of the barform. Each increment of sediment probably accreted during a flood event. Barforms of this nature have commonly been described from low sinuosity or braided river channels.

Localities 1 and 2 show an interesting variety of sedimentary structures which were formed in an ancient major channel system. The sandstone forms virtually continuous exposures which extend north for 0.5km from these localities, and can be examined at a number of points. Sandstone units can be seen that are stacked laterally (multi-lateral bodies) as well as vertically (multi-storey bodies) and contain other examples of low-angle barforms. However, the faces are often dangerous, and it is recommended that they are viewed from a distance rather than close up.

Locality 3 Parton Cliffs (NX 97701990).
From Bransty, follow the track north to Redness Point (Figure 57). This marks the approximate position of the Redness Point Fault, a normal fault which downthrows to the southwest. The cliffs from this point to Parton are formed by the outcrop of the Countess Sandstone, a sandbody of probable Westphalian C age which, according to Eastwood *et al* (1931), is situated approximately 90m above the Bannock Band coal (Figure 58). Follow the track north-eastwards from Redness Point for approximately 0.5km until you reach the ruins of the old Brickworks, now preserved only as foundations. At the base of the cliffs adjacent to the ruins a 4m sequence of dark grey, micaceous siltstones can be seen underlying the sandbody. The siltstone is mainly structureless but does contain occasional thin sandstone streaks and ironstone nodules. The siltstone contains abundant, well preserved plant

material, including specimens of *Calamites, Neuropteris, Annularia* and *Asterophyllites*, some of which occur in original life position.

The presence of structureless siltstones and abundant, well-preserved plant material suggests that these deposits represent rapidly-deposited, sediment-laden overbank flows probably derived from a nearby channel. These overbank events commonly occur during high stage and blanket the plants growing on the channel margins. Similar facies have been recorded elsewhere on the margins of Carboniferous palaeochannels.

The Countess Sandstone may be examined just to the north of the underlying siltstones where it is at least 8m thick. The sandstone is yellow-brown in colour and is dominantly fine to medium-grained. The base is erosional with a relief of about 1m and flute-like scours can be observed on this base. Above this base is a well-developed lag-conglomerate of siderite and coaly masses up to 1m long with fish-tail terminations, which result from the severe compaction undergone by the original peat. Low-angle trough cross-bedding and ripple cross-lamination form the principal sedimentary structures within the sandbody with palaeocurrents directed to the south-west. If the sandbody is followed up the hill 10m to the north, a block of disrupted sediment about 2m across can be examined within the basal lag-conglomerate. Bedding within the block is inclined almost vertically and is folded into a series of open, recumbent folds with a wavelength of about 2cm and sub-horizontal.axial-planar spaced cleavage.

This Countess Sandstone at this locality is interpreted as the deposit of a large river channel which flowed towards the south-west. The presence of abundant coaly clasts at the base suggests that a coal seam, in the form of peat, was eroded through, forming a washout. The channel floor was covered with subaqueous sand dunes and ripples which eventually filled the channel. The block of disrupted sediment was probably emplaced as a result of a channel bank collapse. The folded and cleaved nature of the block is attributed to compaction of the inclined bedding by the weight of overlying sediment.

Locality 4 Tom Hurd Rock (NX 96501825).
This locality is tide-dependant and should ideally be visited at low tide. From locality 3, rejoin your vehicle parked near Bransty and turn right and then right again to join the main A5094 one-way system around Whitehaven. Follow the A5094 Barrow road signs to a set of traffic lights next to the police station. Carry straight on and then take the A5094 Workington road to the right. Take the third turning on the left marked "South Beach Area" and follow the road around past the harbour until you reach a car park (marked P on Figure 57), where the vehicles can be left. Park here and descend to the foreshore via a path which starts by an old cannon to the left of the public conveniences. Tom Hurd Rock forms an isolated outcrop immediately ahead, **which is only exposed at low tides.**

The sequence at Tom Hurd Rock is Westphalian C in age and is approximately 5m thick. Similar sequences can be examined about 20m south in the cliff if it is high tide. The lowest lithology is a dark grey organic-rich siltstone which contains thin sandstone laminations. The siltstone abruptly coarsens upwards to sandstone with the transition marked by abundant trace fossils. The sandstone is about 3m thick and contains current ripples and occasional wave ripples with the top 1m consisting of a set of trough cross-bedding with the foresets orientated towards the southwest. The sandstone forms a sheet which can be traced along the coast for over 150m parallel to the palaeoflow direction.

The abruptly coarsening-upward base, its sheet-like geometry and undirectional palaeocurrents suggests that it was deposited as the result of a major, proximal crevasse splay event. Crevasse splays orginate from the breaching of a channel bank which allows large quantities of sediment and water to flow through a crevasse channel into the interchannel area. This leads to the deposition of a thin sheet sandstone which thins away from the channel. Bedforms are usually unidirectional and orientated away from the crevasse channel, but the presence of wave ripples attests to occasional reworking by waves generated within the interchannel area. The siltstone was probably deposited from the settling of suspended sediment during quiet periods in the interchannel area. The lack of any marine fossils suggests that this area was probably lacustrine. The dark colour of the sediment indicates that conditions were poor in oxygen, although the presence of *Planolites* burrows suggests that fauna could survive within the sediment.

Summary
We have therefore seen evidence for Westphalian sedimentation in a number of distinct environments. These include the deposits of river channels, overbank environments and shallow lakes infilled by crevasse splays and low energy suspension deposits. These environments were commonly followed upon abandonment by the formation of mires now represented by coal seams. Sedimentation at the same time seems to have been dominantly subaqueous and there is little evidence for any marine influence although thin marine bands do occur within the Westphalian.

These types of environments may be compared with an upper delta plain or lower alluvial plain setting, with major channels feeding minor channels. Interchannel areas were occupied by shallow lakes, filled by crevasse splays and lacustrine deltas, with peat mires forming on the infilled lakes and channels.

Locality 5 Saltom Bay (NX 95901610).
From Tom Hurd Rock, rejoin the A5094 one-way system around Whitehaven. Follow the A5094 Barrow road signs to a set of traffic lights next to the police station. Carry straight on and then take the B5345 St. Bees

road to the left. After approximately 0.5 kilometres take the right turning up the hill which is marked Kells Road. At the top of the hill, turn left and immediately park your vehicle on the street. On the right hand side of the road is a large chemical works. Just before the works turn right and walk down a road signposted "Phosphate Rock Vehicles Only". There is a right-of-way by foot. Cross under the railway line and proceed along a path towards a small quarry in the distance behind the works. Where the path splits take a right hand fork and continue down a hill towards the shore. Excellent cliff sections of the Triassic St. Bees Sandstone can be seen ahead of you. At the foreshore turn right and head northeastwards for approximately 300m as far as a wave-cut platform. This is Locality 5.

The lowest unit seen here is a sandstone of Westphalian C age which forms cliffs to the north. The sandstone is mainly purple-grey and contains cross-bedding and ripple cross-lamination with foresets dipping westwards. Erosion surfaces identified within the sandstone in exposures to the north of this locality suggest a channel origin.

Overlying the sandstone is the Basal Breccia of Permian age which is about 2m thick here. The relationship between the Basal Breccia and the Westphalian is one of unconformity with the breccia resting on an uneven surface and infilling widened joints in the underlying sandstone. The unconformity between the Carboniferous sandstones and the Permian Basal Breccia is a consequence of the Variscan Orogeny that took place during late Carboniferous times. This resulted in a period of uplift, erosion and oxidative weathering which was in part responsible for the reddening in the uppermost Westphalian. It was during this episode that widening of the joints in the top of the Westphalian sandstone took place, which were later infilled during the Permian.

The Permian Basal Breccia is a clast-supported polymict breccia which is very poorly sorted and contains a number of poorly-defined beds. Grain size varies from coarse sand to cobbles in a matrix of fine to medium-grained red sand. Clasts are angular to sub-angular, with some imbrication and poorly defined cross-bedding and consist of many different lithologies including Carboniferous Limestone, Westphalian sandstone and siltstone, purple volcanic rocks, white quartzite and conglomerate. The clast types all outcrop locally, and it is likely that the sediment was derived as a consequence of Variscan uplift and erosion of Carboniferous and Lower Palaeozoic rocks situated close to the present position of the Lake District, and deposited by high-energy, fluvial sheetflood events.

Above the Basal Breccia is the Saltom Dolomite Member of the St. Bees Evaporites. This is usually termed the Magnesian Limestone, and is 2.8m thick here. The Saltom Dolomite Member is a yellow brown, well-bedded dolomitic limestone. Fossils are common in certain horizons, especially the bivalves *Schizodus obscurus* and *Bakevellia (Bakevellia) binneyi*. The basal 0.4m contains reworked rock from the underlying breccia. Numerous cavities or vugs and small stylolites are present in the dolomitic limestone.

The presence of the bivalves *Schizodus* and *Bakevellia* suggest a marine environment of deposition. The vugs could be due to either recrystallisation of calcite to dolomite, leading to a resultant volume decrease, or to dissolution of anhydrite nodules formed in an evaporite environment.

This concludes the excursion around Whitehaven. Several sedimentary environments have been encountered from the non-marine upper delta plain/alluvial plain setting of the Westphalian to the early marine phase of the Permo-Triassic. Later sedimentation in the Triassic was exclusively continental with the deposition of the thick succession of the St. Bees Sandstone. Most of the loose boulders on the shore of Saltom Bay are of this sandstone and display a wealth of sedimentary structures. The St. Bees Sandstone can be examined *in-situ* at excellent outcrops both in Saltom Bay and just to the south at St. Bees Head.

REFERENCES

ALLEN, P. M., COOPER, D. C. and FORTEY, N. J., 1987. Composite lava flows of Ordovician age in the English Lake District. *Jl. geol. Soc. Lond.*, **144**, 945-960.

ANDERTON, R., 1982. Dalradian deposition and the late Precambrian-Cambrian history of the N. Atlantic region; a review of the early evolution of the Iapetus Ocean. *Jl. geol. Soc. Lond.*, **139**, 421-434.

ARTHURTON, R. S. and HEMINGWAY, J. E., 1972. The St. Bees Evaporites' — A carbonate-evaporite formation of upper Permian age in west Cumberland, England. *Proc. Yorks. geol. Soc.*, **38**, 565-592.

ARTHURTON, R. S., BURGESS, I. C. and HOLLIDAY, D. W., 1978. Permian and Triassic. In: *The geology of the Lake District,* F. Moseley (ed.), Yorkshire Geological Society Occasional Publication No. 3, 189-206.

BOTT, M. H. P., 1974. The geological interpretation of a gravity survey of the English Lake District and the Vale of Eden. *Jl. geol. Soc. Lond.*, **130**, 309-331.

BOTT, M. H. P., 1978, Deep structure, In: *The Geology of the Lake District,* F. Moseley (ed). Yorkshire Geological Society, Occasional Publication No. 3, 25-40.

BOUMA, A. H., 1962. *Sedimentology of some flysh deposits: A graphic approach to facies interpretation.* Elsevier, Amsterdam. 168 pp.

BRANNEY, M. J., 1988a. A facies interpretation of subaerial explosive volcanism and collapse in the Borrowdale Volcanic Group, SW Langdale English Lake District. PhD Thesis, University of Sheffield.

BRANNEY, M. J., 1988b, Pahoehoe, aa, and block lavas in ancient volcanic sequences in the Lingcove Formation (Ordovician). Borrowdale Volcanic Group, NW England. In press.

BRANNEY, M, J., 1988c. The subaerial setting of the Ordovician Borrowdale Volcanic Group, English Lake District. *Jl. geol. Soc. Lond.*, **145**, 367-376.

BRANNEY, M. J. and SOPER, N. J., 1988. Ordovician volcanotectonics in the English Lake District. *J. geol. Soc. Lond.*, **145**, 367-376.

BRANNEY, M. J. and SUTHREN, R. J., 1988. High level peperitic sills in the English Lake District: distinction from block lavas, and implications for Borrowdale Volcanic Group stratigraphy. *Geol. Journ,* **23**, 171-187.

CAPEWELL, J. G., 1954. The basic intrusions and associated vent near Little Mell Fell, Cumberland. *Trans. Leeds geol. Soc.*, **6**, 243-248.

CAPEWELL, J. G., 1955, The post-Silurian pre-marine Carboniferous sedimentary rocks of the eastern side of the English Lake District. *Q. Jl. geol. Soc. Lond.*, **111**, 23-46.

CAS, R. A. F. and WRIGHT, J. V., 1987, *Volcanic successions: modern and ancient,* Unwin Hyman, London, 528 pp.

CLARK, L., 1964. The Borrowdale Volcanic Series between Borrowdale and Wasdale, Cumberland. *Proc. Yorks. geol. Soc.*, **34**, 343-356.

COCKS, L. R. M. and FORTEY, R. A., 1982. Faunal evidence for oceanic separations in the Palaeozoic of Britain. *Jl. geol. Soc. Lond.*, **139**, 467-480.

COOPE, G. R. and PENNINGTON, W., 1977. The Windermere Interstadial of the Late Devensian. *Phil. Trans. R. Soc. Lond. B*, **280**, 337-339.

COOPER, D. C., LEE, M. K., FORTEY, N. J., COOPER, A. H., RUNDLE. C. C., WEBB, B. C. and ALLEN, P. M., 1988. The Crummock Water Aureole: a zone of metasomatism and source of ore metals in the English Lake District. *Jl geol. Soc. Lond.*, **145**, 523-540.

COX, K. G., BELL. J. D. and PANKHURST, R. J., 1979. *The Interpretation of Igneous Rocks.* George Allen and Unwin, 450 pp.

DAGGER, G. W., 1977. Controls of copper mineralisation at Coniston, English Lake District. *Geol. Mag.*, **114**, 195-202.

DAKYNS, J. R., TIDDEMAN, R. H. and GOODCHILD, J. G., 1897, The Geology of the country between Appleby, and Ullswater and Haweswater. *Mem. Geol. Surv., GB.* 110 pp.

DAVID, W. J. K.,1968. *The Ravenglass and Eskdale Railway.* David and Charles, Newton Abbot.

DEWEY, J. F., 1982. Plate tectonics and the evolution of the British Isles. *Jl. geol. Soc. Lond.*, **139**, 371-412.

DOWNIE, C. and SOPER, N. J., 1972. Age of the Eycott Volcanic Group and its conformable relationship to the Skiddaw Slates in the English Lake District. *Geol. Mag*, **109**, 259-268.

EASTWOOD, T., 1921. The lead and zinc ores of the Lake District. *Mem. Geol. Surv.; Special reports on the mineral resources of Great Britain*, **22**, 56 pp.

EASTWOOD, T., DIXON, E. E. L., HOLLINGSWORTH, S. E. and SMITH, B., 1931. The Geology of the Whitehaven and Workington District. *Mem. Geol. Surv., GB*, 304 pp.

EASTWOOD, T., HOLLINGSWORTH, S. E., ROSE, W. C. C. and TROTTER, F. M., 1968. Geology of the country around Cockermouth and Caldbeck. Mem. Geol. Surv. GB, 298pp.

FALLER, A. M. and BRIDEN, J. C., 1978. Palaeomagnetism of Lake District rocks. In: *The Geology of the Lake District*. F. Moseley (ed.), Yorkshire Geological Society, Occasional Publication No. 3, 17-24.

FIRMAN, R.J., 1954. Note on metasomatic changes in rocks adjacent to the Shap Granite. *Proc. Geol. Assoc.*, **65**, 412-414.

FIRMAN, R. J., 1957, The Borrowdale Volcanic Series between Wastwater and Duddon Valley, Cumberland, *Proc, Yorks, geol. Soc.*, **31**, 39-64.

FIRMAN, R. J., 1972. The Shap area. *Proc. Geol. Assoc.*, **83**, 449-450.

FIRMAN, R. J., 1977. Lake District copper. *Geol. Mag.*, **114**, 483.

FIRMAN, R. J., 1978a. Epignetic Mineralisation. In: *The Geology of the Lake District,* F. Moseley (ed.), Yorkshire Geological Society Occasional Publication No. 3, 226-241.

FIRMAN, R. J., 1978b Intrusions. In: *The Geology of the Lake District,* F. Moseley (ed.), Yorkshire Geological Society Occasional Publication No. 3, 146-163.

FIRMAN, R. J. and LEE, M. K., 1986. Age and structure of the concealed English Lake District batholith and its probable influence on subsequent sedimentation, tectonics and mineralisation. In: *Geology in the real world- the Kingsley Dunham volume,* R. W. Nesbitt and I. Nichol (eds.), Institute of Mining and Metallurgy, London.

FIRMAN, R.J. and LEE, M.K., 1987. The English Lake District batholith-Ordovician, Silurian, Devonian or ? *Geol. Mag.,* **124**, 585-587.

FITTON, J. G. and HUGHES, D. J., 1970. Volcanism and plate tectonics in the British Ordovician. *Earth and Planetary Science Letters*, **8**, 223-228.

FORTEY, N. J. and COOPER. D. C., 1986. Tourmalinization in the Skiddaw Group around Crummock Water, English Lake District. *Mineralog. Mag.,* **50**, 17-26.

FURNESS, R. R., LLEWELLYN, P. G., NORMAN, T. N. and RICKARDS, R. B., 1967. A review of Wenlock and Ludlow stratigraphy and sedimentation in North-West England. *Geol. Mag.,* **104**, 132-147.

GARWOOD, E. J., 1907. Faunal succession in the Carboniferous Limestone of Westmorland. *Geol. Mag.*, **44,** 70-74.

GARWOOD, E. J., 1913. The Lower Carboniferous succession in the North-West of England. *Q. Jl. geol. Soc. Lond.*, **68,** 449-586.

GARWOOD, E. J., 1916. The faunal succession in the Lower Carboniferous rocks of Westmorland and North Lancashire. *Proc. Geol. Assoc.*, **27.** 1-43.

GEORGE. T. N., JOHNSON, G. A. L., MITCHELL, M., PRENTICE J. E., RAMSBOTTOM, W. H. C., SEVASTOPALO. G. P. and WILSON, R. B., 1976. A correlation of Dinantian rocks in the British Isles *Geol. Soc. Lond.,* Spec. Rep. No 7. 87pp.

GOUGH, D., 1965. Structural analysis of the ore shoots at Greenside Lead Mine, Cumberland, England. *Econ. Geol.* **60,** 1459-77.

GRANTHAM, D. R., 1928. The petrology of the Shap Granite. *Proc. Geol. Assoc.* **39.** 299-331.

GUION, P. D. and FIELDING, C. R., 1987. Westphalian A and B Sedimentation in the Pennine Basin, UK. In: B.M. Besly and Kelling G. (eds) *Sedimentation in a Synorogenic Basin Complex - The Upper Carboniferous of Northwest Europe,* Blackie, Glasgow and London, *153-177.*

HARKER, A., 1894, Carrock Fell: A study of the variation of igneous rock masses. Part I, the Gabbro. *Q. Jl. geol. Soc. Lond.*, **50,** 311-77.

HARKER, A., 1895, Carrock Fell: A study of the variation of igneous rock masses. Part II, the Carrock Fell granophyre. Part III, the Grainsgill greisen *Q. Jl. geol. Soc. Lond.*, **51,** 125-48.

HARRIS, P. and DAGGER, G. W., 1987. The intrusions of the Carrock Fell Gabbro Series (Cumbria) as a sub-horizontal tabular body. *Proc. Yorks. geol. Soc.*, **46,** 371-380.

HARRISON, S. and FRITZ W. J., 1982. Depositional features of March 1982 Mount St. Helens sediment flows. *Nature Lond.* **299,** 720-722.

HARTLEY, J. J., 1925. The Borrowdale Volcanic Series of Grasmere, Windermere and Coniston. *Proc. Geol Assoc.*, **36,** 203-226.

HARTLEY, J. J., 1932. The volcanic and other igneous rocks of Great and Little Langdale. *Proc. Geol. Assoc.*, **43,** 32-69.

HARTLEY, J. J., 1941. Geology of Helvellyn and the southern part of Thirlmere. *Jl. geol. Soc. Lond.*, **97,** 129-162.

190   REFERENCES

HELM, D. G., 1970. Stratigraphy and structure of the Black Combe inlier, English Lake District. *Proc. Yorks geol. Soc.* **38**, 105-148.

HITCHEN, C. S., 1934. The Skiddaw Granite and its residual products. *Q. Jl. geol. Soc. Lond.*, **90**, 158.

HOLLAND, E. G., 1981. *Coniston Copper Mines. A field guide.* Cicerone Press, Milnthorpe, Cumbria. 120 pp.

HOUSE, M. R., 1968. Continental drift and the Devonian System. *Inaugural lecture, University of Hull.* 24pp.

HUNTER, R. H., 1980. The petrology and geochemistry of the Carrock Fell Gabbro-Granophyre Complex, Cumbria. Unpubl. Ph.D. Thesis, University of Durham.

HUTT, J. E., 1974-1975. The Llandovery graptolites of the English Lake District. *Palaeontological Society (Monograph)*, Part 1 (1974), 1-56; Part 2 (1975) 57-131.

INESON, P. R. and MITCHELL J. G., 1974. K-Ar isotopic age determinations from some Lake District localities. *Geol. Mag.*, **111**, 521-37.

INGHAM, J. K., McNAMARA, K. J. and RICKARDS, R. B., 1978. The Upper Ordovician and Silurian Rocks. In: *The Geology of the Lake District*, F. Moseley (ed.), Yorkshire Geological Society, Occasional Publication No. 3. 121-145.

IRVINE, T. N., 1982. Terminology for layered intrusions, *J. Petrol.*, **23**, 127-62.

IIXER, R. A., STANLEY, C. J. and VAUGHAN, D. J., 1979. Cobalt, nickel and iron bearing sulpharsenides from the north of England. *Mineralog. Mag.*, **43**, 359-395.

JACKSON, D. E., 1961. Stratigraphy of the Skiddaw Group between Buttermere and Mungrisdale, Cumberland. *Geol. Mag.*, **98**, 515-528.

JACKSON, D. E., 1962, Graptolite zones in the Skiddaw Group in Cumberland, England. *J. Palaeontol.* **36**, 300-313.

JACKSON, D. E., 1978. The Skiddaw Group. In: *The Geology of the Lake District*, F. Moseley (ed.), Yorkshire Geological Society, Occasional Publication No. 3, 79-98.

JEANS, P. J. F., 1971. The relationship between the Skiddaw Slates and the Borrowdale Volcanics. *Nature: Phys. Sci.*, **234**, 59.

JEANS, P. J. F,.1972. The junction between the Skiddaw Slates and the Borrowdale Volcanics in Newlands Beck, Cumberland. *Geol. Mag.*, **109**, 25-28.

KOKELAAR, B. P., 1982. Fluidisation of wet sediment during the emplacement and cooling of various igneous bodies. *Jl. geol. Soc. Lond.*, **139**, 21-33.

LAWRENCE, D. J. D., WEBB, B. C. YOUNG, B. and WHITE, D. E., 1986. The geology of the late Ordovician and Silurian rocks (Windermere Group) in the area around Kentmere and Crook. *Report British Geol. Surv.*, **18**, No 5, 32pp.

LEE, M. K., 1986. A new gravity survey of the Lake District and a three dimensional model of the granite batholith. *Jl. geol. Soc. Lond.*, **143**, 425-435.

MacDONALD, R. and WALKER, B. H., 1985. Geochemistry and tectonic significance of the Lower Carboniferous Cockermouth lavas, Cumbria. *Proc. Yorks. geol. Soc.*, **45**, 141-146.

MacDONALD R., MILLWARD, D., BEDDOE-STEPHENS, B., and LEYBOURN-PARRY, J., 1988. The role of the tholeiitic magmatism in the English Lake District: evidence from dykes in Eskdale. *Mineralog. Mag.*, **52**, 459-472.

MARR J. E., 1916a. *The Geology of the Lake District*. Cambridge University Press, Cambridge. 220pp.

MARR, J. E., 1916b. The Ashgillian succession in the tract to the West of Coniston Lake. *Q. Jl. geol. Soc. Lond.*, **71**. 189-204.

MARR, J. E. and Nicholson, H. A., 1888. The Stockdale Shales. *Q. Jl. geol. Soc. Lond.*, **44**, 654-732.

MASON, R., 1988. Did the Iapetus Ocean really exist? *Geology*, **16**, 823-826.

McKERROW, W.S. 1982. The northwest margin of the Iapetus Ocean during the early Palaeozoic, *Mem, Am. Assoc. Petrol, Geol.*, **34**, 521-533.

McNAMARA, K. J., 1979. The age, stratigraphy and genesis of the Coniston Limestone Group in the Southern Lake District. *Geol. Jl.*, **14**, 41-67.

MILLWARD, D., 1979. Ignimbrite volcanism in the Ordovician Borrowdale volcanics of the English Lake District. In: *The Caledonides of the British Isles.* Geological Society, London, 629-634.

MILLWARD, D., 1980. Three ignimbrites from the Borrowdale Volcanic Group. *Proc. Yorks. geol. Soc.*, **42**, 595-616.

MILLWARD, D., MOSELEY, F. and SOPER, N.J., 1978. The Eycott and Borrowdale volcanic rocks. In: *The Geology of the Lake District*, F. Moseley (ed.), Yorkshire Geological Society, Occasional Publication No. 3, 99-120.

MILLWARD D. and LAWRENCE, D. J. D., 1985. The Stockdale (Yarlside) Rhyolite - a rheomorphic ignimbrite? *Proc. Yorks. geol. Soc.*, **45**, 299-306.

MITCHELL, G. H., 1940. The Borrowdale Volcanic Series of Coniston, Lancashire. *Q. Jl. geol. Soc. Lond.*, **96**, 301-319.

MITCHELL, G. H., 1956. The Borrowdale Volcanic Series of the Dunnerdale Fells, Lancashire. *Liverpool and Manchester Geological Journal.*, **1**. 428-449.

MITCHELL, G. H., 1956. The geological history of the Lake District. *Proc. Yorks. geol. Soc.*, **30**, 407-463.

MITCHELL, G. H. 1970. The Lake District. *Geologists' Association Guide No. 2* Geologists' Association, London. 1-42.

MITCHELL. G. H., MOSELEY, F., FIRMAN R. J., SOPER, N. J., ROBERTS, D. E., NUTT, M. J. C., and WADGE, A. J., 1972. Excursion to the northern Lake District. *Proc. Geol. Assoc.*, **83**, 443-470.

MITCHELL, M., TAYLOR, B. J. and RAMSBOTTOM, W. H. C., 1978. Carboniferous, In: *The Geology of the Lake District*, F. Moseley (ed.),Yorkshire Geological Society, Occasional Publication No. 3. 168-188.

MOLYNEUX, S. G., 1988. Micropalaeontological evidence for the age of the Borrowdale Volcanic Group. *Geol. Mag.*, **125**, 541-542.

MOLYNEUX, S. G. and RUSHTON, A. W. A., 1984. Discovery of Tremadoc rocks in the Lake District. *Proc. Yorks. geol. Soc.*, **45**, 123-127.

MOLYNEUX, S.G. and RUSHTON, A. W. A., 1988. The age of the Watch Hill Grits (Ordovician), English Lake District: structural and palaeogeographical implications. *Trans. Roy. Soc. Edinburgh*, **79**, 43-69.

MOSELEY, F., 1960. The succession and structure of the Borrowdale Volcanic rocks south-east of Ullswater. *Q. Jl. geol. Soc. Lond.*, **116**, 55-84.

MOSELEY, F., 1964. The succession and structure of the Borrowdale Volcanic rocks north-west of Ullswater. *Geol. Jl.* **4**, 127-142.

MOSELEY, F., 1968. Joints and other structures in the Silurian rocks of the Southern Shap Fells. *Geol. Jl.* **6**, 79-96.

MOSELEY, F., 1972. A tectonic history of North-West England. *Jl. geol. Soc. Lond.*, **128**, 561-598.

MOSELEY, F., 1975. Structural relations between the Skiddaw Slates and the Borrowdale Volcanics. *Proc. Cumb. Geol. Soc.*, **3**, 127-145.

MOSELEY, F. (ed.), 1978. *The Geology of the Lake District.* Occasional Publication No. 3, Yorkshire Geological Society, Leeds, 284pp.

MOSELEY, F., 1981(a) *Methods in Field Geology.* Freeman, 211 pp.

MOSELEY, F., 1981(b) Field meeting to the northern Lake District. *Proc. Yorks. geol. Soc.*, **43**, 395-410.

MOSELEY, F., 1982. Lower Palaeozoic volcanic environments in the British Isles. In: *Igneous rocks of the British Isles*, D. Sutherland (ed.), Wiley, Chichester, 39-44.

MOSELEY, F., 1983. *The volcanic rocks of the Lake District.* Macmillan, 111p.

MOSELEY, F., 1984. Lower Palaeozoic lithostratigraphic classification in the English Lake District. *Geol. Jl.*, **19**, 239-247.

MOSELEY, F., 1986. *Geology and Scenery in the Lake District.* Macmillan, 88pp.

MOSELEY, F., 1988. The Ordovician batholith of the English Lake District. *Geol. Mag.*, *125*.

MOSELEY, F and AHMED, S. M., 1967. Carboniferous joints in the north of England and their relation to earlier and later structures. *Proc. Yorks. geol. Soc.*, **36**, 61-90.

MOSELEY, F. and MILLWARD, D., 1982. Ordovician volcanicity in the English Lake District. In: *Igneous Rocks of the British Isles,* D. Sutherland (ed.), Wiley, Chichester, 93-111.

NORMAN, T. N., 1963. Silurian (Ludlovian) Palaeo-current directions in the Lake District area of England. *Bull. Geol. Soc. of Turkey*, **8**, 27-54.

NUTT, M. J. C., 1966. Field meeting in the Haweswater area. *Proc. Yorks. geol. Soc.,* **35**, 429-433.

NUTT, M. J. C., 1968. The Borrowdale Volcanic Series and associated rocks around Haweswater. *Proc. Geol. Soc. Lond.*, **1649**, 112-113.

NUTT, M. J. C., 1972. Haweswater. *Proc. Geol. Assoc.*, **83**, 463-467.

OLIVER, R. L., 1954. Welded Tuffs in the Borrowdale Volcanic Series, English Lake District, with a note on similar rocks in Wales. *Geol. Mag.*, **91**, 473-48.

194 REFERENCES

OLIVER, R. L., 1961. The Borrowdale volcanic and associated rocks of the Scafell area, English Lake District. *Q. Jl. geol. Soc. Lond.*, **117,** 377-417.

PENNINGTON, W., 1977. The late-glacial flora and vegetation of Britain. *Phil. Trans. R. Soc. Lond.*, **B. 280,** 247-271.

PENNINGTON, W., 1978. Quaternary Geology. In: *The Geology of the Lake District,* F. Moseley (ed.), Yorkshire Geological Society, Occasional Publication No. 3, 207-225.

POSTLETHWAITE J., 1918. Mines and mining in the Lake District, 3rd Edit., W. H. Moss, Whitehaven, 164 pp.

RAISTRICK, A., 1925. The Glaciation of Borrowdale. *Proc. Yorks. geol. Soc.*, **20,** 155-181.

RAMSBOTTOM, W. H. C., 1977. Major cycles of transgression and regression in the Namurian. *Proc. Yorks. geol. Soc.*, **41,** 261-291.

RICKARDS, R. B., 1970. The Llandovery (Silurian) graptolites of the Howgill Fells, northern England. *Palaeontogr. Soc. Monogr.*, 1-108.

RICKARDS, R. B., 1973. On some highest Llandovery red beds and graptolite assemblages in Britain and Eire. *Geol. Mag.*, 110, 70-72.

ROBERTS, D. E., 1971. Structure of the Skiddaw Slates in the Caldew Valley, Cumberland. *Geol. Jl.*, **7,** 225-238.

ROBERTS, D. E., 1977a. The structure of the Skiddaw Slates in the Blencathra-Mungrisdale area, Cumbria. *Geol. Jl.*, **12,** 33.

ROBERTS, D. E. 1977b. Minor tectonic structures in the Skiddaw Slates of Raven Crags, Mungrisdale, northern Lake District. *Proc. Geol. Assoc.,* **88,** 117.

ROBERTS, D. E., 1983. Metasomatism and the formation of greisen in Grainsgill, Cumbria, England. *Geol. Jl.*, **18,** 43.

ROSE, W. C. C. and DUNHAM, K. C., 1978., Geology and hematite deposits of South Cumbria. *Mem. Geol. Survey. G. B.*

RUNDLE, C. C., 1979. Ordovician intrusions in the English Lake District. *Jl. geol. Soc. Lond.,* **136,** 29-38.

RUNDLE, C.C. 1981. The significance of isotopic dates from the English Lake District for the Ordovician-Silurian time scale. *Jl. geol. Soc. Lond.*, **138,** 569-572.

SCHMINCKE, H. U., 1967., Fused tuffs and peperites in south-central Washington. *Geol. Soc. Am. Bull.*, **78,** 319-330.

SELF, S. and SPARKS, R. S. J., 1978. Characteristics of widespread pyroclastic deposits formed by the interaction of silicic magma and water. *Bulletin Volcanologique*, **41**, 196-212.

SHACKLETON, E. H., 1966. *Lakeland Geology*. Dalesman, Clapham, North Yorkshire, 128pp.

SHACKLETON, E. H., 1975. *Geological Excursions in Lakeland*. Dalesman, Clapham, North Yorkshire.

SHAW, W. T., 1970. *Mining in the Lake Counties*. Dalesman, Clapham, North Yorkshire.

SHEPHERD, T. J., BECKINSALE, R. D., RUNDLE, C. C. and DURHAM, J., 1976. Genesis of the Carrock Fell tungsten deposits. Cumbria: fluid inclusion and isotope study. *Trans. Inst. Min. Metall.* (Section B. Appl. Earth Sci.) **85**, B63.

SHIPP, T. (ed.), 1982. *The Lake District*. Cumberland geol. Soc., George Allen and Unwin, 136pp.

SIMPSON, A., 1967. The stratigraphy and tectonics of the Skiddaw Slates and the relationship of the overlying Volcanic Series in part of the Lake District. *Geol. Jl* **5**, 391-481.

SMITH, R. A., 1974. A bibliography of the geology and geomorphology of Cumbria. Cumberland geol. Soc., 1-32.

SOPER, N. J., 1970. Three critical localities on the junction of the Borrowdale Volcanic rocks with the Skiddaw Slates in the Lake District. *Proc. Yorks. geol. Soc.*, **37**, 461-493.

SOPER, N. J., 1987. The Ordovician batholith of the English Lake District. *Geol. Mag.*, **124**, 481-483 and 483-484.

SOPER, N. J. and HUTTON, D. H. W., 1984. Late Caledonian sinistral displacements in Britain: implications for a 3 plate collision model. *Tectonics*, **3**, 781-794.

SOPER, N. J. and MOSELEY, F., 1978. Structure. In: *The Geology of the Lake District*, F. Moseley (ed.), Yorkshire Geological Society, Occasional Publication No 3. 45-67.

SOPER, N. J. and NUMAN, N. M. S., 1974. Structure and stratigraphy of the Borrowdale Volcanic rocks of the Kentmere area, English Lake District. *Geol. Jl.,* **9**, 147.

SOPER, N. J. and ROBERTS, D. E., 1971. Age of cleavage in the Skiddaw Slates in relation to the Skiddaw aureole. *Geol. Mag.*, **108**, 293-302.

SOPER, N. J., WEBB, B. C. and WOODCOCK, N. H., 1987. Late Caledonian (Acadian) transgression in north-west England: timing, geometry and tectonic significance. *Proc. Yorks. geol. Soc.*, **46**, 175-192.

SPARKS, R. S. J. and WALKER, G. P. L., 1977. The significance of vitric-enriched air fall ashes associated with crystal-enriched ignimbrites. *J. Volcanology and Geothermal Research*, **2**, 329-341.

STANLEY, C. J. and VAUGHAN, D. J., 1982, Mineralization in the Bonser Vein, Coniston, English Lake District: mineral assemblages, paragenesis and formation conditions. *Mineralog. Mag.*, **46**, 343-350.

STILMAN, C. J., 1984, Ordovician volcanicity. In: *Aspect of the Ordovician System*, D. L. Bruton. (ed.). Palaeontological Contributions from the University of Oslo. No. 295, 183, 194.

STRENS, R. G. J., 1965. The graphite deposit of Seathwaite in Borrowdale, Cumberland, *Geol. Mag.*, **102**, 393-406.

SUTHREN, R. J. 1977. Volcanic and Sedimentary facies of part of the Borrowdale Volcanic Group, Cumbria. Unpublished PhD thesis, University of Keele.

SUTHREN, R. J., and FURNES, H., 1980. Origin of some bedded welded tuffs. *Bulletin Volcanologique*, **43**, 61-71.

WADGE, A. J., 1972. Sections through the Skiddaw-Borrowdale unconformity in eastern Lakeland. *Proc. Yorks. geol. Soc.*, **39**, 179-198.

WADGE, A. J ., 1978. Classification and Stratigraphical relationships of the lower Ordovician rocks. In: *The Geology of the Lake District*. F, Moseley (ed.), Yorkshire Geological Society, Occasional Publication No, 3, 68 - 78.

WADGE, A. J. 1978. Devonian. In: *The Geology of the Lake District*, F. Moseley (ed.), Yorkshire Geological Society, Occasional Publication No 3, 164-167.

WADGE, A. J., GALE, N. H., BECKINSALE, R. D. and RUNDLE, C. C., 1978. A Rb-Sr isochron for the Shap granite. *Proc. Yorks. geol. Soc.*, **42**, 297-305.

WADGE, A. J., HARDING, R. R. and DARBYSHIRE, D. P. F., 1974. The rubidium-strontium age and field relations of the Threlkeld Microgranite. *Proc. Yorks. geol. Soc.*, **40**, 211-222.

WADGE, A. J., NUTT, M. J. C. and SKEVINGTON, D., 1972. Geology of the Tarn Moor tunnel in the Lake District. *Bull. Geol. Surv. G. B.*, **41** 55-73.

WALTHAM, A. C., 1974. *The limestone and caves of north-west England.* Charles, Newton Abbot. 477pp.

WARD, J. C., 1876. The geology of the northern part of the English Lake District. *Mem, Geol. Surv., UK*, 132pp.

WEBB, B. C., 1972. N-S trending pre-cleavage folds in the Skiddaw Slates Group of the English Lake District. *Nature: Phys. Sci.*, **35**, 138-140.

WEBB, B. C. and COOPER, A. H., 1988. Slump folds and gravity slide structures in a Lower Palaeozoic marginal basin sequence (the Skiddaw Group) NW England. *Jl. Struct. Geol.*, **10**, 463-472.

WEBB, B. C. and LAWRENCE, D. J. D. 1986. Conical fold terminations in the Bannisdale Slates of the English Lake District. *Jl. Struct. Geol.*, **8**, 79-86.

WEBB, B. C., MILLWARD, D., JOHNSON, E. W., and COOPER, A.H., 1987. The Ordovician batholith of the English Lake District. *Geol. Mag.*, **124**, 482-484.

WILSON, J. T., 1966. Did the Atlantic close and then reopen? *Nature, Lond.*, **211**, 676-681.

YOUNG, B., 1984. Geology and history of Nab Gill Mine, Eskdale, Cumbria. *Proc. Cumb. geol. Soc.*, **4**, 269-275.

YOUNG, B., 1985a. Mineralisation associated with the Eskdale Intrusion, Cumbria. *Report Programme Directorate A, British Geological Survey.* No. PDA2 85/3.9.

YOUNG, B. 1985b. Greisens and related rocks associated with the Eskdale Granite, Cumbria. *Report Programme Directorate A. British Geological Survey.* No. PDA2 85/2.

YOUNG, B., 1987. *Glossary of the minerals in the Lake District and adjoining areas* (Newcastle upon Tyne: British Geological Survey).

YOUNG, B., in press. Wavellite and Variscite from Scar Crag Cobalt Mine, Cumbria. *Proc. Cumberland Geol. Soc.*

YOUNG,. B., ANSARI, S. M. and FIRMAN, R.J . 1988, Field relationships, mineralogy and chemistry of the greisens and related rocks associated with the Eskdale Granite, Cumbria. *Proc. Yorks. geol. Soc.* **47,** 109 - 123.

GLOSSARY

This glossary contains only those names which are less common or those which are particularly significant to the Lake District.

Accretionary lapilli. Pea-sized pellets of ash with a concentric internal structure caused by accretion of damp ash in an eruption cloud. In the Lake District previously referred to as Bird's Eye Tuff.

Agglomerate. Coarse pyroclastic fall deposits accumulating near to a vent (should include bombs or some other indication of the proximity of the vent). It is a term often misused to refer to any coarse pyroclastic deposit.

Amygdaloidal. Igneous rocks (usually lavas, sills, dykes, etc.) in which vesicles (gas cavities) have been infilled by other minerals (e.g. calcite, chlorite or zeolites).

Andalusite. Aluminum silicate formed mostly in pelitic rocks by thermal metamorphism. In the Lake District (variety chiastolite) it is best seen in the Skiddaw Slates within the aureole of the Skiddaw Granite.

Andesite. Fine grained intermediate igneous rock. In the Lake District often porphyritic with plagioclase and, less commonly, pyroxene phenocrysts. Occasionally amygdaloidal.

Aureole. See metamorphic aureole.

Basalt. These rocks, within the Lake District, mostly have tholeiitic affinities and grade into basaltic andesite. Commonly dark grey, fine grained, with small phenocrysts and flow jointing.

Batholith. Large granitic intrusions which, within the Lake District, are largely subsurface, and of Ordovician and Devonian age.

Bedded Tuff. Essentially a field term referring to bedded volcaniclastic sediments. Can include lacustrine, fluviatile, marine, fall and surge deposits.

Boudins. Thin competent beds alternating with incompetent strata may be broken into sections and torn apart under the action of strong stresses.

Bouma sequences. Refer to turbidite sequences which are often repeated in a cyclic fashion. Includes graded beds, parallel lamination, cross and convolute lamination, with siltstones and mudstones. Designated A to E.

Caldera. A large volcanic crater usually many kilometres in diameter. Can be formed by explosion or collapse after magma withdrawal, generally with the production of complex structures.

Caledonian orogeny. Those episodes of mountain building which affected the area extending from the Appalachians to Norway between Late Precambrian and Devonian times. Several phases have been recognised in the Lake District with the climax during the early Devonian.

Cleavage. Rock cleavage is the regular splitting of rocks following the application of high stress. In the Lake District this is usually a spaced cleavage (fracture cleavage), which principally affects the finer grained rocks.

Clints. The bare surfaces of limestone pavement between grykes.

Conjugate folds. Contemporaneous minor folds whose axial planes are adjacent but make an angle of about 60 degrees to each other.

Convolute bedding. Complex small scale folds formed by slumping during turbidity flow. Common in the Skiddaw Slates and Coniston Grits.

Cordierite. A Mg-Al-silicate most commonly developed in the Skiddaw Slates within the aureole of the Skiddaw Granite.

Crenulation cleavage. Small folds or wrinkles on cleavage planes with wave lengths of a few millimetres or less.

Cross-lamination. (Cross-bedding). Bedding planes inclined to the principal bedding planes as with current ripples, etc. Mostly in sandstones and siltstones.

Cumulates. Formed in layered intrusions. Crystals generally settle to the floor of the magma chamber and ideally solidify in layers from the base upwards. There are many varieties and terms in use, some of which are as follows -

1. Cumulus crystals — primocrysts often attached to a boundary surface of an intrusion.

2. Inter-cumulus liquid and layering — refers to the trapped liquid surrounding cumulus crystals. May crystallise as new minerals.

3. Rhythmic layering — repetition of a particular type of cumulate layer.

4. Cryptic layering — chemically graded layering. Upward change in composition of solid solution minerals with fractionation, e.g. plagioclase becomes more sodic.

See Cox, Bell, and Pankhurst, 1979.

Cyclothem. A series of beds deposited during a single sedimentary cycle. These cycles are often repeated as in the Yoredale Group.

Dacite. Fine grained acid igneous rock. Frequently white weathering with a glassy devitrified groundmass. Can exhihibit flow banding and jointing, and in the field can be difficult to distinguish from rhyolite and certain ignimbrites.

Debris flow (lahar, mudflow). Viscous mass flow of debris capable of supporting large clasts. May be subaerial or subaqueous and a result of water torrents, earthquakes, or volcanic activity. Volcanic mudflows (lahars) are often hot when deposited.

Diabase. A field term for altered dolerite or micro-diorite.

Ductile. Incompetent materials. Strata which deform easily.

Ensialic arc. A line of volcanoes resulting from the destruction of oceanic crust beneath a continent.

Epiclastic. In volcanic terrains, refers to normal processes of erosion, transport and redeposition rather than those of volcanic eruption.

Eutaxitic. A typical texture of ignimbrite with dark streaks (fiamme) in a fine grained, white weathering matrix.

Evaporite. A rock composed of minerals such as halite and gypsum, and typically formed by evaporation in inland desert basins.

Fall deposits. See pyroclastic fall.

Faults. Faults of many varieties are to be found in the Lake District.

a) Normal — high angle faults with predominant dip slip movement and downward movement of the hanging wall.

b) Reverse — as above but with upward movement of the hanging wall.

c) Wrench — near vertical faults with predominant strike slip movement (note also oblique slip).

d) Thrust — low angle faults often with younger formations forced above older.

e) Slide — Associated with olistostromes. Downward movement of rock masses under the influence of gravity.

f) Volcanotectonic — faults activated by volcanic activity.

Fiamme. Lenticular streaks of the eutaxitic texture of an ignimbrite. They are lens shaped in three dimensions and represent flattened pumice fragments.

Flame structures. Flame like structures in bedding produced by turbidity flow. Mostly seen in greywacke siltstones.

Flow banding. Streaky bands of flow seen in lavas, sills and other igneous rocks.

Flow breccia. Brecciated margins to viscous lava. The lava surface solidifies but is fragmented and rafted along by pressure from the still-liquid interior.

Flow jointing. Joints which are parallel to the flow of lavas and sills. The joints may be cooling effects and are not necessarily contemporaneous with the actual flow.

Flute cast. Flute like sole marks which are elongate and bulbous at one end. Especially seen on lower surfaces of greywacke sandstone units.

Fluviatile. Sediment deposited from running water (rivers or streams).

Folds. There are many varieties in the Lake District some of which are as follows-

1. Monocline — a fold with one near vertical limb and one near horizontal limb (British terminology).

2. Recumbent folds — folds with near horizontal axial planes. In the Lake District the Skiddaw Slates display many such folds which are sideways closing and have a near horizontal cleavage.

3. Disharmonic. When incompetent and competent strata are folded together there are ductility contrasts. The incompetent beds are formed into smaller scale and more complex folds.

4. Slump. Formed by sedimentary processes when unconsolidated or partially consolidated sediments collapse or flow downslope.

5. Flow. Formed by flowage in igneous rocks (generally lavas, sills and dykes). Can resemble slump folds.

Graded bedding. Bedding in which there is upward gradation in grain size from coarse at the bottom to fine at the top. Usually seen in greywacke sandstone units.

Granophyre. Medium grained granitic rock with a micrographic texture.

Greisen. A rock rich in quartz, white mica, topaz and fluorite produced by the pneumatolysis of granite.

Greywacke. Clastic rock, usually sandstone or siltstone, but with a wide range in grain size. Generally a product of turbidity currents.

Groove casts. Sole marks, usually where a long straight furrow has been filled in by sand (greywacke).

Grykes. Fissures, usually about one metre deep produced by chemical weathering of limestone. In Carboniferous Limestone they usually form along joints, the orientation of which was controlled by regional tectonics.

Hercynian. The earth movements (orogeny) which extended from eastern America and across southern Europe from Devonian to Triassic Times. The Lake District was marginally affected by these earth movements at the end of the Carboniferous.

Heterogeneous. Usually refers to materials of varying composition in a rock.

Hornfels. Hard fine grained rock produced by thermal metamorphism, in the Lake District Skiddaw Slates are locally metamorphosed to this grade by the Skiddaw Granite.

Iapetus. An ancient ocean which was supposed to have formed to the north-west of the Lake District during Cambrian and Ordovician times.

Ignimbrite. A deposit of a pumiceous pyroclastic flow. In the field some ignimbrites are difficult to distinguish from dacite and rhyolite. See also eutaxitic texture and fiamme.

Karst. Topography typical of limestones with clints, grykes, pot holes and caves.

Lacustrine. Sediment deposited in lakes.

Lahar. See debris flow.

Lapilli. Volcanic fragments 2-60mm in diameter formed by volcanic eruption.

Layered intrusions. See cumulates.

Metamorphic aureole. The zone of thermally metamorphosed rock surrounding an igneous intrusion, most notable in larger intrusions.

Metasomatism. Change in composition of a rock by percolating solutions. New minerals are formed.

Olistostrome. A deposit which includes large rafts of rock often more than 1000m in diameter, which become detached and slide downslope under the influence of gravity.

Orogeny. A period of mountain building during which rocks may be strongly folded, cleaved and subjected to metamorphism.

Pelite. Mudstone (clay or silt rock).

Peperite. (Schmincke 1967). Complex quench fragmentation of magma in contact with water saturated sediment. It can occur at the base of lavas where it resembles flow breccia, but in the Lake District is more significant in the identification of sills, where the breccia at top contacts includes igneous fragments entirely supported by sediment.

Phenocrysts. Large crystals in a porphyritic igneous rock.

Phreatic deposit. Product of volcanic steam-explosivity

Phreatomagmatic. Volcanic explosivity resulting from interaction of hot magma and groundwater (or steam).

Piedmont. The foot of a slope, escarpment, or mountain range.

Pneumatolysis. Alteration of rocks and the formation of new minerals by emanation of gases and vapours derived from solidifying igneous rocks.

Poikilitic. An igneous texture in which larger crystals have numerous inclusions of smaller crystals.

Polygenetic. Usually refering to rock made up of materials (fragments) of different composition, e.g, polygenetic breccia.

Polyphase structures. Complex folds and other structures produced by more than one phase of deformation.

Porphyritic. An igneous rock which has larger crystals (phenocrysts) set in a finer matrix.

Porphyroblasts. Large crystals in a metamorphic rock.

Posthumous structures. Structures in younger rocks which have the same orientation as those in older rocks and are presumed to have been derived by reactivation of those structures.

Psammite. Sandstone.

Pseudomorph. A crystal which has been replaced by another mineral by chemical alteration *in situ*.

Pyroclastic. Fragmental ejecta from a volcanic explosion.

Pyroclastic fall deposits. Fragmental material falling to earth after explosive eruption.

Pyroclastic flow. A dense lateral flow of pyroclasts and gas from a volcanic source.

Pyroclastic surge. See surge.

Rheomorphic Tuff. Tuff formed by ash which was so hot on deposition that it was able to flow like a lava following welding.

Shield volcano. Large convex pile mostly lava. The slopes are gentle, composition generally basaltic, and the eruption either central vent or flank.

Sill. Near concordant sheet-like igneous intrusion. Many of the sills intruded into Borrowdale volcanics were shallow intrusions into unconsolidated wet ash.

Strato-volcano. Composite volcano with repeated pyroclastic and lava vent eruption. Characteristic of subduction zones and adjacent volcanic arcs.

Subduction zone. The zone at an oceanic trench where one plate slips down beneath another.

Surge deposit (pyroclastic surge). Volcanic surface blast which transports pyroclastic materials in ground-hugging turbulent flow. A variety of bedforms such as cross-stratification is characteristic.

Tuff. Lithified ash (fragments less than 2mm in diameter) originally deposited by pyroclastic fall. Material reworked by fluviatile and other processes is not strictly tuff.

Turbidite. A rock deposited from a turbidity current. A slurry of mud and sand flowing down-slope under water.

Volcaniclastic: Clastic rock (sandstone, siltstone, etc.) formed by reworking of volcanic deposits by sedimentary processes.

Volcanic breccia. A rock consisting of large angular volcanic fragments which may have been formed by a variety of processes.

Welded Tuff. Tuff formed by the agglutination of hot ash.

Xenolith. Foreign rock fragment, caught up in an igneous magma.

INDEX

NOTES

NOTES

NOTES